Renting Lacy

A Story of America's Prostituted Children

by Linda Smith
with Cindy Coloma

Foreword by Ernie Allen
President of The National Center For Missing and Exploited Children

Some names have been changed to protect the identities of the women and children we serve.

ISBN 0-9765594-6-3

Cover and text art by J. David Ford & Associates, Hurst, TX

Printed in the United States of America.

Shared Hope International
P.O. Box 65337
Vancouver, WA 98665
www.sharedhope.org

Table of Contents

Acknowledgements

This book needed a title that really shouted to the world the plight of children in slavery. Early one morning as I finished writing, I expressed my frustration to my husband Vern over not yet finding a title that would help people understand how children were being sold right here in America. After a few moments of reflection, he said, "They are not being sold outright by their trafficker; these girls' young bodies are being rented out by the hour."

Thus, the title *Renting Lacy*. Thank you, Vern, for helping craft just the right title, and thank you for reading the early drafts to help me understand how men might respond.

Early on, I was told by several that the book as written could be too intense, and even repulse and anger readers. I took this concern to Ernie Allen, President of the National Center for Missing and Exploited Children. After listening several minutes, Ernie thoughtfully encouraged me to err on the side of keeping it accurate to the truth I had discovered, even if it meant rejection by some. Finding a way to write the truth of the horrible things that happen to these children while not causing such strong revulsion that people would put the book down was a constant struggle. Thank you, Ernie, for speaking for the missing and exploited children who cannot speak for themselves. Your advice helped shape this book.

Thank you Sheila Avery, Nancy Winston, Pastor Ron Hart, David and Marjie Austen, Reverend David White, James Varner, Joe Varella, Robin and Ross Gunn, Beverly Morin, Juana Killion, and Jan Kennedy for suffering through some of the early drafts and delivering your "at times" painful but helpful observations, suggestions, and edits. Because of you, readers are more likely to finish the book and act on what they learn.

There are no words to express the admiration I have for our research team, led by Samantha Healy-Vardaman and Melissa Snow. This book is based on in-depth research performed by Shared Hope International from 2006 to 2009, resulting in *The National Report on Domestic Minor Sex Trafficking: America's Prostituted Children*, published in June 2009. Without Samantha's and Melissa's leadership, the shocking findings and resulting *National Report* would not be possible. Thank you, Samantha and Melissa. *Renting Lacy* would not stand on the strong foundation of truth without you.

Thank you to my friends – survivors who will not be named here – for digging into your pain-filled lives as sexually exploited children so I could understand and express more accurately the lives of the hundreds of thousands of children held in sex slavery. Thank you for taking the suffering from your childhood and turning it into hope for the victimized women and children of today.

ADDITIONAL INFORMATION and RESOURCES
• *The National Report on Domestic Minor Sex Trafficking: America's Prostituted Children*
• *Protected Innocence Initiative*

Foreword

To millions of Americans, the trafficking of children for commercial sexual purposes only happens somewhere else — in Southeast Asia or Central America — not on Main Street USA. Yet, it is abundantly clear that today at least 100,000 American children are being used as commodities for sale or trade in cities across the nation. These kids are 21st Century slaves. They cannot walk away.

A quarter-century ago, a police commander said to me, "The only way not to find this problem in any community is simply not to look for it." The good news is that America has begun to look. The bad news is that millions still do not understand the depth and severity of this problem. They don't understand what really happens to these kids, or that these kids come from families just like ours.

My hope is that this book will change all of that. Linda's tenacity and advocacy for those who are trapped in these situations has already roused many to action, but this book will awaken far more. She tells the stories in the style of a novel, and in a manner that leaves no room for misunderstanding. She helps those who doubt the existence of such criminal enterprises trading on the young to see. These accounts are gripping and shocking. They convey the horror and hopelessness that so many American kids face on the streets of our cities.

Linda neither glamorizes the lives these kids are required to live, nor does she demonize them. She portrays them exactly as they are, as victims who desperately need and deserve rescue.

Some will be shocked. Some will be outraged. Some will be saddened. My hope is that *all* will be spurred to action.

Ernie Allen
President and CEO, National Center for
Missing and Exploited Children

Introduction

I didn't want to touch the foul-smelling girl, and I certainly didn't want to dramatically change my life.

More than 10 years ago, my days were crammed with policy, legislation, and serving my constituents as Congresswoman Linda Smith representing Washington State's Third Congressional District. But in the midst of my hectic schedule, five days opened up — and I was able to squeeze in a trip to India.

It wasn't a pleasure trip. I was going because a missionary had told me about the commercial sex industry — forced prostitution — and I was going to see for myself. Could it really be as bad as he said?

I would soon discover it was worse than I could have imagined or believed.

Those five days transformed my life.

On Falkland Road in Mumbai, I was stunned by the reality of the sex trade industry. Children and women lined streets where raw sewage flowed in uncovered ditches. I found young girls, mere children, locked in rooms deep within brothels, or several stories up behind barred windows, waiting for the men who "like them young."

One girl in particular would change me.

She was just a wisp of a thing, filthy, alone. The conditions of her life were deplorable. The scent of a thousand men was upon her. She was about the age of my granddaughter.

I am doomed forever, her eyes said to me, *beyond help, beyond hope.*

And then, I heard a still, small voice telling me to touch her.

I denied it, but the voice returned.

Finally, I reached for her.

My mind had been changed already, shocked and scarred by the images on Falkland Road. But in the instant I touched this child — as she fell into my arms — my heart was branded. Feeling the frail humanity of her heartbeat against mine, I knew I had to do something.

I returned to the United States. My supporters had planned for me to run for another political office. Instead, my life took a radical turn. Within weeks I created a non-profit corporation, Shared Hope International. Here, my husband Vern and I — and as many friends as I could convince to join us — put together our assets and resources to create homes for girls ... girls like the one I had held in my arms that first life-changing night.

I discovered that many of these little girls had been brought to India all the way from Nepal. As impossible as it seemed, most had actually been sold by their own parents — duped into believing they would have good work and a better life. Others had literally been kidnapped, stolen.

In every case, the cause was the same: someone had to supply product for the hungry sex markets in Mumbai.

My heart broke for these little Nepalese girls; they wanted to go home, home to their own culture, the familiar food, the familiar climate. So I began reaching out to ministries in Katmandu, and we began opening homes in Nepal as well.

But India and Nepal were only a first taste ... only an introduction into human trafficking and the sex trade industry. I would soon find that this horror stretches around the world. And after five years of work in the field, I came into a new, perhaps even more awful, shock: this nightmare was happening in my own backyard.

This wasn't just an India problem. It wasn't just an international problem. It was also a United States problem.

Where did the sex trade industry come from? How can this happen in America? Why isn't it stopped? What can be done? Can hope be found?

This book offers some answers. But the bottom line is very simple, and very terrible. The human trafficking of children is occurring every day in the United States. It is happening in your town and mine — all over the nation.

And it is happening in greater volume than one can hardly imagine.

I'll tell you the stories. I'll introduce you to the victims and their tormentors. You'll meet the victims' families, the law enforcers, even the buyers of children.

It will not be pretty, and it will not be easy. But it will be the truth.

I've presented them here in story form because this is how life really happens in the world of human trafficking. The language is rough, vulgar in places. I don't wish to offend anyone, especially not those who have given so generously down through the years to enable the work of Shared Hope International. In fact, deeply conservative people of great propriety and dignity are among our strongest supporters — the people for whom I thank God every day — and yet these are the ones perhaps most at risk of taking offense at the words on these pages. Yet I pray for their understanding and pardon, because this book is tragically necessary. After more than a decade of undercover investigations, extensive research, generating a million words or more in reports and articles and media interviews and testimony before Congress and international conferences — all to plead for action against the human traffickers — it is clear to me that only the harshness of the truth can wake the world to this horror. It will take a real-life confrontation with the agony these children are living through. It will take a painful but authentic look into the ugly underworld. Then, perhaps — and I hope and pray — people will rally to the cause of putting a stop to it all.

So the stories you'll read in these pages are true. They are compiled from actual events. Of course, for the protection of innocent people, I've altered names and other details. And as for the profane language, rest assured that I have already "toned it down" considerably; the actual transcripts would be even more terrible.

Along the way, I'll offer comments and insights from my decade of experience in the field. (As a matter of convention, I'll refer to the children as females and the buyers as males; this is overwhelmingly the case, but it's also true that occasionally we encounter boys as victims and women as buyers.)

I offer this book for the sake of the girls I've found trapped in slavery, the girls we've rescued, the girls to whom we've been able to give a fresh start — and the thousands upon thousands of girls we have yet to reach. If the journey you're about to take with me can inspire you to help us help even one of them, it will have been worth the risk, worth any effort, any sacrifice.

I invite you, I urge you, to pull that girl close. Hold her in your arms. Feel her heartbeat. Remember her face. Join us in saving her life.

"May heaven's rich blessing come down on everyone,
American, English or Turk,
who will help to heal this open sore of the world."
—*David Livingstone's final plea*
to abolish the slave trade in Africa, 1873

Glossary of Terms

To understand the terrible truth about human trafficking, we have to understand the terrible terms. This will be uncomfortable, perhaps, but to view this awful other world accurately requires us to listen to some things we'd rather never hear.

This, then, is a glossary for the world we're about to enter.

Trafficker/Pimp — anyone who receives money or something of value for the sexual exploitation of another person.

Facilitator — any business or person allowing a trafficker/pimp to carry out his exploitations. These facilitators — taxi drivers, hotel owners, newspapers where girls are advertised — work in direct and indirect partnerships with pimps and enable the commercial sexual exploitation of children.

Buyer — anyone who pays for or trades something of value for sex. This can be a family member, teacher, baseball coach, and member of the clergy — anyone, male or female.

Survival Sex — a situation involving a homeless youth who trades a sex act with an adult in exchange for basic needs such as shelter, food, etc. Knowing that homeless youth are unable to work legally and provide for themselves, sexual predators commonly target them, taking advantage of their vulnerability. The Trafficking Victims Protection Act (TVPA) defines a "victim" of sex trafficking as any child under the age of 18 and involved in a commercial sex act where money or something of value is given to or received by any person. Accordingly, "survival sex" actually qualifies as domestic minor sex trafficking.

Quota — a set amount of money that a trafficked girl must make each night before she can come "home." Quotas are often set between $300 and $2,000. If the child returns without meeting the quota, she is typically beaten or sent back out.

Automatic — the victim's routine when her pimp is out of town, in jail, or otherwise not in direct contact with those he is prostituting. Victims are expected to be "on automatic," and they generally comply — either out of fear of punishment or because they have been psychologically manipulated into a sense of loyalty or love. All money generated "on automatic" is turned over to the pimp when he returns.

Bottom Bitch — one girl, among several controlled by a single pimp, appointed by him to supervise the others, report rule violations, and sometimes even help inflict punishment on them.

Brothel, Bordello, Cathouse, Whorehouse — a large apartment or a house where sex is sold; in some cases, a facility specifically designed for selling sex on the premises. Such a site often features extreme security measures intended to prevent attacks by other criminals seeking the large amounts of cash and drugs kept there — and to keep the women and children in. The facilities often are guarded (and open) 24 hours a day, but some have closing times in which the victims are locked in from the outside.

Caught A Case — a pimp or a prostituted person has been arrested and charged with a crime.

Choosing Up — the process by which a different pimp takes "ownership" of a victim. Choosing up actually occurs simply by making eye contact with another pimp (which is why eye contact with other pimps is strictly prohibited). If the original pimp wants the victim back, he must pay a fee to the new pimp. It's the victim, however, who is then required to "work" to pay restitution to her original pimp. And usually the debt is increased — as a penalty for the disrespect of the original pimp that "choosing up" represents.

Circuit (or Track) — a set area known for prostitution activity. This can be a local term: the area around a group of strip clubs and pornography stores, or a particular stretch of street. Or it can be a series of cities among which prostituted people are moved — one example would be the West Coast circuit of San Diego, Las Vegas, Vancouver (British Columbia), and the cities between. The term can also refer to a chain of states, such as the "Minnesota pipeline" by which victims are moved through a series of locations from Minnesota to markets in New York.

Daddy — what pimps require their victims to call them. (See *Family or Folk*.)

Date — the exchange when prostitution takes place, or the activity of prostitution. A victim is said to be "with a date" or "dating."

Escort Service — an organization, operating chiefly via cell phone and increasingly the Internet, which sends a victim to a buyer's location (an "outcall") or arranges for the buyer to come to a house or apartment (an "in-call"); this may be the workplace of a single woman or actually a small brothel. Some escort services are networked with others and can assemble large numbers of women for parties and conventions. Some serve those with fetishes, such as sex with children or sadomasochism.

Exit Fee — money a pimp demands from a victim who is thinking about leaving. This is routinely an exorbitant sum intended to discourage her departure. (Victims usually don't have money, other than what the pimps give to them to supply their needs.) Most pimps never let their victims leave freely.

Family or Folk — a group of people under the control of one pimp; he plays the role of father or "Daddy." This idea can be extremely complicated psychologically for a victim who has never had a supportive family.

Finesse Pimp — one who prides himself on controlling others primarily through psychological manipulation. Even in such cases, however, the threat of violence is always present.

The Game — the subculture of prostitution. "The game" functions as a fully formed subculture, complete with established rules, hierarchy, and language. People who do not actively participate in "the game" are viewed as not understanding how it works nor understanding the people involved in it.

Gorilla (or Guerilla) Pimp — one who controls his victims almost entirely through violence.

Ho Line — a loose network of inter-city or interstate communication between pimps, chiefly by phone, used to trade, buy, and sell prostituted women and children. A ho line uses frequently changing slang and code words to confound law enforcement.

John or Buyer — a person paying another for sexual gratification, control, and/or domination. The term "john" comes from the alias often used by customers in order to remain anonymous. The john drives the entire system. Without a buyer, there wouldn't be a seller and there wouldn't be a victim. The demand for commercial sexual services fuels the problem of domestic minor sex trafficking. Victims of domestic minor sex trafficking are forced to sell their bodies to meet this demand.

Kiddie Stroll (or Runway) — an area featuring prostituted children under 16, often much younger.

The Life — the experience of being used as a victim in prostitution.

Lot Lizard — a derogatory term for a person who is prostituted at truck stops.

Madam — an older woman who manages a brothel. The madam has usually been prostituted in her earlier years; she may be a pimp herself, perhaps a career criminal.

Reckless Eyeballing — same as *Choosing Up*.

Renegade — a prostituted person not under the control of a pimp. Renegades are usually vulnerable to threats, harassment, and violence intended to make them "choose" a pimp. The term also sometimes refers to a victim who violates a pimp's rules.

Seasoning — a combination of psychological manipulation; intimidation; gang rape; sodomy; beatings; deprivation of food or sleep; isolation from family, friends, and other sources of support; and threatening or holding hostage of a victim's children. Seasoning is designed to totally break down a victim's resistance and ensure that she will do anything she is told.

Sister Wife, Sister-in-Law, Wife-in-Law, Stable Sister — what women in a pimp's "stable" call each other. (See *Family or Folk* and *Stable*.)

Stable — a group of victims under the control of a single pimp. (The choice of a farming word is worse than ironic, in that pimps indeed treat their victims like animals.)

Trade Up, Trade Down, Buy and Sell — to move a victim like merchandise. Pimps are quick to get rid of victims who cause problems, or who no longer match the profile sought by the clientele that the pimp serves. A pimp may trade straight across, or trade with some exchange of money, or trade one victim in return for two or more other victims. The sale price for a victim is usually $2,500 to $3,500. The victims can be moved long distances rapidly — with a guard, overnight, and/or by air.

Trick — the act of prostitution; also the person buying it. A victim is said to be "turning a trick" or "with a trick."

Turn Out — to be forced into prostitution; also a person newly involved in prostitution.

Chapter 1

Dreams on the Track

Lacy and Star — Las Vegas, Nevada

Lacy thought the girl sitting on the edge of the bed might cry.

"You need more eyeliner," Lacy said, trying to distract her. She picked up a black pencil and lifted Star's chin. "Baby, you look like an actress. Like that girl you like so much. What's her name?"

"Miley Cyrus?" Star asked, looking up with a hopeful gaze.

Lacy darkened the black line around Star's eyes. "That's the one who plays Hannah Montana, right?"

Star nodded. She stopped biting her lip and looked at herself in the mirror. "I want to be an actress and singer someday."

Lacy smiled — how many times had they heard this? Cherry called Star the "Little Diva."

"If you work hard, you can do anything," Lacy assured her. "Bobby has connections, good ones. And you're getting experience in acting. It's called the school of life, you know."

Lacy could see the girl's mind at work as she contemplated this.

"Next week, Bobby has you lined up for a photo shoot," she added quickly. "But you gotta work your butt off for this stuff. It's hard work, no doubt, girl, but we all gotta do our part. The more you want somethin', the harder you gotta work."

Lacy could see her words taking effect. Star nodded and settled on the edge of the hotel bed. She smoothed her black mini skirt and zipped up her tall silver boots.

"How long will I be out tonight?" Star looked at the clock: it was 8 p.m.

Lacy flipped on the television and handed Star the remote.

"Just till you meet your quota. Sometimes I'm done by midnight, other nights it takes till morning. But you're looking fine, girl. I think it won't be a long night for you at all."

Star, channel-surfing, pulled her feet in cross-legged on the bed. Lacy eyed her. Her push-up bra didn't have much to work with — but it looked good enough through the sheer, low-cut blouse. Lacy considered taking off the girl's fishnet stockings. Bobby always told her, though, the girls couldn't go wrong with fishnet anything. Star's full blonde curls reminded Lacy of those young beauty pageant girls who look like they're playing dress-up. But Star could walk well in her high-heeled boots, like she'd been doing it her whole life. The combination of innocent and slut would make her a hit with the johns; that was a certainty.

"You remember what I told you, right?"

The girl nodded, though her eyes were on an MTV reality show. Lacy sighed. Man, this girl took some work.

"Let's go through it one more time." Her voice was stern, to remind Star who was in charge.

Star's eyes moved from Lacy back to the television. "When Bobby calls, I meet Bobby and the trick at room 18," she recited. "I have the hotel key in my boot, and I'll ask if the guy wants to party; then once in the room, I ask if he's a cop. Bobby gets the money, and you'll be here if I need you." It was the singsong of a gradeschooler. "I gotta watch the time and I should try getting the trick to pay for more or ask for another girl to join us. He's got to pay for everything first. If business is slow, then I'll go out with you later on."

Lacy smiled a bit. Maybe this one was quicker than she looked. "And what do you do?"

Star rolled her eyes. "I know this."

"We're doing our final sound check, like on a movie set or before a concert."

Star sat up straighter. "I don't look any other pimp in the eyes, or else."

"Yeah, or else you end up in some other stable," Lacy warned, "with a pimp who won't treat you so nice as Bobby."

"I know. I wouldn't do that, not ever."

Still, Lacy kept rehearsing the rules, until she felt sure Star was prepared for her first night out — prepared as she could be, anyway. At one point, her own mind flashed back to her first week at work — and a shiver ran through her back.

"Star, you've got it better than half the girls out there," Lacy said. "Our man is good to us. Bobby won't beat you unless you don't obey. He'll keep getting your nails done and buy you nice stuff. We'll probably all go to Disneyland for Christmas. We went last year."

But now, as the word *Christmas* settled in, Lacy saw Star turn back to the TV, her eyes changing. Lacy sighed. She knew this young girl probably had Christmas memories: snow and presents, a Christmas tree, church plays, cookies and milk for Santa Claus. And someone — a mom or dad, an aunt or someone — fondly remembered in the scene.

Lacy needed to shift the picture. "Have you ever been to Disneyland?" she asked brightly. "Ever see Tinker Bell or ride Pirates of the Caribbean?"

"No. My dad was supposed to take me there, but he never could afford it."

Lacy wasn't surprised. She had known that routine herself. "Well, Bobby can afford it," she replied. "You're really lucky Bobby found you. Who knows what would've happened to you?" Star nodded. Just the night before, they'd seen Candy beaten and stomped down by her pimp until she was nearly unconscious.

Lacy's phone buzzed on the dresser. "Looks like it's time to work. Ready?"

Star bit her lip again. *If this kid cries*, she thought, *I'll beat her myself.*

"I'm ready," Star announced. "And you don't have to say it; I know: the customer is always right, blah, blah, blah. Men are just *disgusting*, though," she added with something like a snarl. "Except for Bobby."

Lacy couldn't help but laugh. "Yeah, you got that right. You're what, 12? — and you figured that out already?"

"Thirteen next month," Star frowned.

"Well," Lacy sighed, "there are girls out there who started younger than that, like I was. You just tell those disgusting men whatever age they want to hear, and do whatever they want. You can practice your acting."

"The first 20 or so times were the hardest. Then you sort of get used to it and you don't think as much about it."
—Former child sex trafficking victim from Kansas City, Missouri

Chapter 2

Prayers in the Night

Doris in Lincoln, Nebraska

Doris adjusted her glasses and leaned toward the row of children's faces on the computer screen.

"There she is," Patty said. She reached over Doris's shoulder and pointed to one of the faces. Doris focused. Suddenly she covered her mouth.

"Oh Cassie," she whispered.

It felt like a slap in the face, seeing her granddaughter's face on a website for missing children. Every day, Cassie's empty room had reminded her of the loss — but this was different. Now Cassie was among those other babies, just one more of those other innocent faces, each one with someone back home in the same agony she'd been feeling every moment, every day, every night.

"It's great they got her on there at least," Patty said. "Better than what the police are doing," she added with a look of disgust. "I know they've got their hands full, but we're the ones paying their salaries with our hard-earned money." Patty reached around again, to move the mouse over Cassie's face. She clicked on "See Poster." Cassie's "missing persons" poster filled the screen.

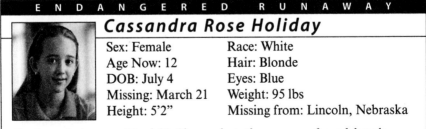

ENDANGERED RUNAWAY		
Cassandra Rose Holiday		
	Sex: Female	Race: White
	Age Now: 12	Hair: Blonde
	DOB: July 4	Eyes: Blue
	Missing: March 21	Weight: 95 lbs
	Height: 5'2"	Missing from: Lincoln, Nebraska

Cassie was last seen on March 21. She may be in the company of an adult male. They may still be in the local area or they may travel to Las Vegas.

(Sample only. Model was used for photograph. This is not an actual missing persons report.)

"What!" Doris's hands began to shake. "Why does it say that — about the adult male and the Las Vegas?" She wished she could turn off the computer, but she couldn't stop staring at her granddaughter's sixth grade school picture ... the sparse facts and description of her life ... the huge words: ENDANGERED RUNAWAY.

Patty sat heavily in the chair beside her. "I'm sorry, Doris. I told them about Cassie and that fella her friends kept seeing her with."

Doris turned sharply. "Why did you say that? They'll think she's one of those bad kids."

Her mind was churning. Yes, she knew Patty was trying to be helpful. They'd attended mass together for decades. Patty had been there for her when Walter died. But sometimes her helpfulness bordered on nosiness. What right did she have to tell them those terrible rumors about her granddaughter?

She turned back to the screen. "Why does it say Las Vegas?" Doris repeated helplessly. "That's awfully far away, and Cassie doesn't know anyone there."

"Don't you remember that the fella is known in Las Vegas?"

Doris shook her head. Maybe she had heard that, once — but it was all too much, simply too much.

"He's known as a pimp in that area," Patty went on, "and he was in Lincoln for his grandmother's funeral. Cassie's friends identified him as her boyfriend."

"No, no, no," Doris groaned, shaking her head. "Cassie is *12 years old*. She's not allowed to have a boyfriend — especially after that incident with the Olsen boy. They have this all wrong. They'll be looking in the wrong direction."

Patty pulled her chair closer to Doris. "Sweetie, we're no good to Cassie if we don't look at what's really going on," she said quietly. "The police said that the pimps start out by acting like they're a girl's boyfriend."

Doris couldn't stop shaking her head in confusion and pain. An older boyfriend who was really a pimp? She simply couldn't believe that.

"My Cassie," she moaned, "she would never do something like that."

But a seed of doubt had already crept in. Cassie had been acting strangely. Sneaking make-up, talking back. And Doris had found those see-through panties in the wash. Cassie didn't want to practice the piano anymore. Instead, she sang and danced routines in her bedroom, with the door locked.

But wasn't that normal for her age?

"They say," Patty sighed, "these men are very good at what they do."

"These men?"

"Yes, the pimps. They go after girls who're lonely, the ones who have 'low self-esteem.' They even kidnap some of them. I guess some kids are still missing after those hurricanes. It's horrible what's going on. They take these kids and force them into being prostitutes, and—."

Patty made a sudden stop.

"I'm sorry, Doris, I wasn't thinking."

But Doris couldn't bring herself to believe it. Not a 12-year-old. Why would anyone do such terrible things to a little girl like that? Sure, her little granddaughter had been watching MTV more — Doris had been thinking of turning off the cable television, it was so destructive to children these days — but Cassie still watched Nickelodeon half the time!

Doris pointed to the computer screen. "Why don't they say more about who Cassie really is — that she plays Beethoven beautifully, or that she wants to sing or be an actress, or that she played Annie in a school play? She collects porcelain dolls and spoons...."

Patty wrapped her arms around her friend, but Doris felt as if she'd become an empty shell. *At any moment, I'll just shatter, into a million pieces*, she thought. *And what a relief that will be.*

Finally Doris felt herself able to calm down. She gulped hard and tried to close off her mind to the horror. She needed to see some facts.

"How do I get back to that first page?" she demanded. Patty leaned over her again and moved the mouse to a button that said "Home."

"I want to see how many kids are missing," Doris said sharply.

The U.S. Department of Justice reports:
- **797,500 children (younger than 18) were reported missing in a one-year period of time studied resulting in an average of 2,185 children being reported missing each day.**
- **203,900 children were the victims of family abductions.**

- **58,200 children were the victims of non-family abductions.**
- **115 children were the victims of "stereotypical" kidnapping. (These crimes involve someone the child does not know or someone of slight acquaintance, who holds the child overnight, transports the child 50 miles or more, kills the child, demands ransom, or intends to keep the child permanently.)**[1]

Doris wanted to vomit.

Here they sat, in her little extra bedroom, with all these horrible things going around them.

"How can this be possible?" she whispered. "This is America. This says 1.6 million children run away — or were thrown away — last year. That many kids have terrible lives?" Her throat tightened. "And who throws away a child?"

Patty was shaking her head, wiping away tears. They kept scrolling through the stories, a seemingly endless stream of tragedies.

"It's because we don't follow after God," Patty finally said. "It's because everybody has lost their morals. Back when we were children, it was the worst offense to be out drinking and dancing a little. Now it's so terrible out there — all the sexual immorality that's considered normal."

Doris could only shake her head in agreement, feeling swamped by despair. "If my Walter were alive today," she mumbled, "he'd die of shock at the country he fought for, back when men were honorable."

Patty choked back her tears. "Oh Doris, I'm very sorry about all of this."

Doris couldn't help but remember what people had said when Walter died. They were all *very sorry*.

"You took her in and raised her right," Patty said. "Sometimes children just get with the wrong people."

The hopelessness of it all descended heavily on Doris.

"So you think many of these kids come back to their families?" she asked quietly.

---

[1]   National Center for Missing and Exploited Children website.

"Sometimes they do." Patty stirred a bit. "There's probably a lot of ways to help find Cassie. We can't give up."

Doris was murmuring. "She got in with the wrong crowd. I thought it was a phase, and then it just got out of hand." She folded her shaking hands together. "So what do I do now?"

Patty pointed to the computer. "They have support groups. And programs in case we want to volunteer."

Doris didn't answer. She was tired lately. The cancer was beginning to move through her. Patty didn't know. Cassie hadn't even known about it, when she....

And once Doris was gone, she now realized, there would be no one looking for her beloved granddaughter. No one at all.

Commentary — How A Child Becomes A Product

I've spent countless hours in the ugly underbelly of the trafficking world, and its language and customs are still repulsive to me. But I have also had the advantage of seeing the end of the story — and I cheer to see lives amazingly saved and restored, to see girls discovering that they have not lost the person God made them to be, and to see many of them now reaching back into the darkness to pull others from slavery. So the repugnant encounters, in the end, turn out to be a "small price to pay." This kind of redemption, from this kind of bondage, is worth everything.

Tanya used filthy language telling me about her first night on the street, and how she had been seasoned, prepared for the experience — her first step into the blackness of a new life in prostitution. Her horrific experience is commonplace in the hidden realms of the human trafficking world. The seasoning process may be long or short, depending upon the individual, and what it takes to bring her to the point of dehumanization and subjugation — but in any case, seasoning involves *words*. The girl is taught a new language that would be outrageously wrong in her old life. It's a language filled with crude descriptions, words, and phrases.

But it's also more than words — because during seasoning, the girl is also instructed, forced, into the *knowledge* of sexual depravity. As Tanya made clear to me, a girl is routinely gang-raped and beaten, and shaped by psychological manipulation.

It is trial by fire. Education by torture.

By the time it's all over, using bad language is the least of the girl's concerns. She is devastated — and desperately wants the pain to stop.

We see a "hooker" on the street and we're disgusted. We read or hear the language of prostitution and we're appalled. But what we don't realize is the extremes of anguish that have led to this nauseating end.

And so — to understand clearly — we have to go back to the beginning. To the "why" of prostitution. It's simple supply and demand. There is a buyer who wants a product.

For that product to come to market, the seller — the pimp, the facilitator, the trafficker — must prepare his product to meet the demand. He does this by first obtaining a raw product, then preparing and packaging the product, and finally distributing the product, offering it for sale.

And the product? Usually a girl. Usually around the age of 11 to 14. Here's the process....

Obtaining Product (Child)

A number of strategic practices are used to obtain children for sex trafficking, and more tactics are being developed as the demand for children continues to rise in the U.S.

As to location, it's cheaper and less risky getting a girl from a small town or a city in the U.S. than to import women and children from other countries.

A trafficker gets a child by:

1. Abduction — sometimes right off the streets, other times after a period of luring (the girl may believe the pimp is a boyfriend, then one day the "boyfriend" lures or forces the girl to leave her home or hometown).

2. Coercion — which is still a form of abduction. This is when a child is lured into the life. The girl may believe that she's willingly chosen to go with the pimp and to do the things he or a facilitator ask her to do. She is usually not aware of the physical and psychological brainwashing she's being subjected to.

Preparation of Product (Child)

As with any product, the seller seeks to meet the desire of the buyer. In this case, the buyer desires a young girl who appears to be equal parts innocent child and slut.

-   Innocent — a little girl's age alone makes her an innocent. This element is natural. Even among girls who have been in "the life" for years, I always find "layers" of the children they really are ... perhaps in the way they giggle, or the way they long for a mother figure. Even after years of abuse and deprivation, the innocent child can be perceived.

- Slut/Whore — this part *doesn't* come naturally. A little girl doesn't grow up as the product that buyers want her to be — she is by no means a slut or a whore. She doesn't have a sexually depraved mind or sexual desires. Someone — a pimp, facilitator, porn producer, and/or molester — must forcibly *condition* the girl to *become* this way. This is product preparation.

So how does someone turn an innocent little girl into a "slut"?

- Language — the unique language used in the commercial sex industry is, to us, crude and vile. To them, it's the norm.
- Pornography — this is used in two ways: for the enticement of the buyer, and for the preparation of the child who will be bought.
   - Child pornography often increases a person's desire for sex with girls and boys. The direct link is clearly evident. Most buyers of children have spent extensive time viewing children in sexual situations. This creates an expectation that the child he buys should live up to.
   - Pornography is used to train a child in how to behave, what to say, how to sound, how to *seem*. Children are forced to watch and learn.

Packaging of Product (Child)

- Language — The child must adopt the new language, the dialect of the street. She must be able to use the crude language that the buyer expects, to initiate the fantasy, exciting him and inciting him to use her — yet at the same time keeping him from a desire beyond his sexual hunger, which might make him want to rescue her from her pimp.
- New name — The child is usually given a new street name designed to provoke the fantasy. Her old name is discarded. She is now Lacy, Star, Cherry, Sugar, or some such.

- Appearance — a girl is dressed and made up in the manner which a buyer expects and desires — as a "schoolgirl," a "little beauty queen," a "sexy child," a "woman in a child's body."

I have to admit that at times, this all sounds beyond belief. For us living our regular lives, raising families, striving in our careers, going to college, planning vacations, it's as if these children and women exist in another dimension. We may pass a gentlemen's club or see a girl dressed in a manner that makes us question — *she's not really a slave, is she?* — and yet, it's true. Our research, our investigations, have revealed a reality that still doesn't seem possible in our own towns, in our own nation.

Bear with me as we unveil these children's realities, the words they are trained to use, and the deeds they are forced to do. Let's look beneath the make-up and clothing, the hard language, the sexy act ... to see who these girls really are — and to see if we can help.

Chapter 3

First Night Out

Star in Las Vegas, Nevada

Star was happy. The plan for the night had changed. Bobby had lined up something special. He had picked her up. He was driving her down the Strip!

Since her arrival, she hadn't seen Bobby as much in Vegas as back in Lincoln. Now, she had to share him with his other girls — which had been a total shock to her. But he promised it would change, and soon.

Bobby was talking on the phone. "When do we get some time alone?" Star whined. His hand flew up in her direction. Star winced and jerked her head back, knocking it against the window. But at least he hadn't hit her. Star knew, Bobby never liked to hit her. She remembered how he had almost cried once, after he had punched her in the face and sprained her arm. She knew it was his father's fault that Bobby couldn't control his temper. He'd seen so much violence as a boy.

"Sorry," she whispered. Bobby was a businessman; she knew better than to interrupt.

And why, in that very moment, did she think of her grandma? Oh, God. Grandma would be worried sick. Star could just picture her compulsively making tea, trying to sooth away the worries. *I should call*, Star thought, *tell her that everything's okay*. But then Grandma would want her to come home, of course. Or maybe there'd be a bug on her phone and the police would take her away. Bobby said that could happen.

Bobby drove with his wrist on the steering wheel. Star stared out the windows — looking out front, out both her window and his. She loved the canals at the Venetian. Maybe after tonight, she and Bobby would take a ride in one of the boats, with the Italian guy singing! On the other side of the street, Star spotted the fountains in front of the Bellagio. Sometimes the water danced, in a magical routine, set to music that filled the air. It was like nothing she'd seen in Lincoln, Nebraska. Star imagined strolling there with Bobby like the other couples, holding hands and kissing as the water sprouted and exploded like fireworks.

"Wouldn't it be fun—?" Star stopped. Bobby's menacing glare shut her mouth. He kept talking into the phone. Something about a big FBI bust.

All around her, lights were flashing, the faces of famous people and beautiful showgirls beaming from billboards. There was the rollercoaster at New York, New York. There was the giant pirate ship, with crowds all around it, right beside the street. Vegas was better than Hollywood, Bobby had told her; and she believed it. It would be easier to get her big break here too.

Bobby slapped the cell phone shut. "Do a good job tonight, okay, baby?" His tone was smooth and caring again. Star knew Bobby loved her. He had told her again and again. She just needed to be more professional when he was doing business.

"I will, Bobby." He turned a corner and pulled around to the back of a huge shimmering hotel. Beside a door, they slowed to a stop. He turned and took her chin in his hand, staring long into her eyes, just like he'd done the first night they went on a date.

"You're well-trained," he said with a grin and raised eyebrow. "Just imagine you're with me."

Star smiled shyly.

"Yes, that's exactly how you need to look," he said. "Innocent. That little girl innocence drives me crazy, baby."

Star knew she had to do this. Had to do her part toward making them reach their dreams — though she wished Bobby would just drive away with her, and somehow they'd be rich and together *right now*.

"Just knock at that back door there, and someone will let you in. It's room 315. When you're done tonight, you sleep with me, okay?"

Star smiled at that. Lacy would be mad, but Star didn't care. In the week since she started living with Bobby, she hadn't once slept in his bed for the entire night. He hardly ever even wanted to have sex with her now — which

Star didn't mind, except ... she wondered if he didn't love her as much now. Still, whenever she asked him, Bobby said he did.

Lacy, though — she was always in Bobby's bed. And sometimes one or two of the other girls. Star understood she was the new girl; she hadn't earned any status — that's what Lacy had told her, anyway. Bobby said he wished she could be with him — that was nice — but they had rules to follow, to keep the business running right. Lots of late nights, early mornings after work, Star dropped into her lonely bed but couldn't sleep: Vegas was noisy. She lumped up pillows against her chest, imagining Bobby's warm body. She wanted to sleep behind him, curled against him, with her heart beating against his strong back. "Spooning" — she'd heard it called that. On those rare moments she had spooned with Bobby, before he pushed her away, Star felt the world outside stop. Those were the moments of perfect peace, when she was safe from everything bad.

"You have something in you, Star," Bobby was saying. "I don't know what it is, but it's a spark of something rare. I think you and I will be together a long time." His voice was like butter. "Lacy and the other girls are getting older. And not just that, I really think you could become something great. I've got your photo shoot set for next week."

Star took a sharp breath. This was a thrill. Moments like this reminded her that *good always comes from bad* — that's what her grandma always said. Some of this stuff was hard, but good would come from it.

"This guy here — room 315 — he's very important," Bobby went on. "I trust you to make him happy. And if he's happy, we'll both be happy. He's a movie director — big name, but I can't tell you who. And remember to never ask. Just do your best work, okay?"

Star was pleased. Bobby did trust her. She could tell he really believed in her. Back home, Grandma was always telling her to keep her head out of the clouds. Her mom, she was sure, she would've told her to go after her dreams — but her mom was gone. Dead for five years already. Only Bobby understood. He'd even given her this big important client for her first night!

Star turned down the visor to see what she looked like. Lacy had done a nice job. Her make-up was perfect. Her blonde hair looked full and silky.

"I'll pick you up in a few hours," Bobby said.

The night was still warm. Star tried to walk like Julia Roberts in *Pretty Woman.* Someday they'd do a remake of that movie, and she was determined to play the lead. She knocked lightly on the gray door, glancing back to see Bobby watching from the car. He was making sure she got inside — which made her smile. She waved at him just as the door cracked open.

The guy looked her up and down — a dark-skinned man with wide shoulders, massive muscles, in a tight T-shirt. Star felt small walking through the little space between him and the open door. She pulled out a "Ben Franklin" like Bobby had told her, and handed it to the man. He frowned and took it quickly.

"This way," he said. Star wished for one last look at Bobby sitting in the car outside. She wondered if he'd be waiting when she returned.

They were in the storage area of a hotel. Stacks of food and cleaning supplies were lined up in rows. After a few turns, the man cracked open another door and motioned for her to go through.

"Take the elevator at the end of the hall."

Star didn't ask questions; she just hurried through the door. It shut immediately behind her. Her stomach was doing that fluttery thing it did, like right before she went onstage for *Annie.* Which end of the hall? she wondered. First she went to the right, but when that turned into another long hallway, she turned around. When she found the elevators, they were shimmering in gold, so polished that she could see her own reflection.

What floor was 315 on? The bouncer at the door had only said to take the elevator. She stared at the buttons and pushed the number "3" — why not?

The elevator opened first at the main floor. An older couple stepped in. They stared at her, then looked at one another. As the doors opened to the third floor, Star was stunned by the sight of a huge candelabra, a marble floor and shiny gold trimmings. She hadn't even thought to take a step when the door started closing. She zipped out just in time.

The room numbers started with 3s. She was pretty proud. She'd found it, all by herself.

Following the arrows, she walked down a carpeted hallway. She suddenly felt like she really was Julia Roberts in the movie. Her heart started beating faster as she stopped in front of the door. She needed to get into her part; this was all training. And maybe the man behind the door would be Richard Gere! Or, even better, a younger version of him. Actors, Lacy had told her, often request "escorts."

But as she knocked, she hoped no one would answer.

The door opened to a good-looking guy with dark hair and blue eyes, and a smile that made Star's heart skip a beat — even as she thought of Bobby. She'd never betray Bobby, never — but still, it was nice that this guy was so well-dressed. And his cologne smelled real nice too.

"Come on in," he said. Star noticed the drink in his hand. "I was beginning to think you weren't coming."

"Sorry, it took me a bit to find it." She stepped inside to a suite that looked almost as big as Grandma's house. It had a living room, and she could see one, and then two, bedrooms. Through double doors she could see a bathroom with a huge tub. Just like the one in *Pretty Woman*! She wondered if she'd get to take a bath later. Maybe she'd ask if it would be okay.

"Let's go in here," the man said, motioning to one of the bedrooms. The sound of a woman moaning filled the room. The television was on. Star saw a number of naked people having sex on the TV. She figured this was an "orgy," from what the other girls had talked about.

Star remembered her line. "So," she asked, "wanna party?"

"Yeah," the guy chuckled, "I want to party." He sat in a chair in the corner. Star wondered what she should do next.

"You a cop?" she asked — then she remembered Lacy telling her to watch how she talked with the higher priced customers. "I mean, are you a cop?"

He was laughing. "You only have to ask that when you're on the street, or — well, not here. But no, I'm not a cop. You really are new at this."

Star bit her lip. "My first night."

"And I'm your first customer?" He turned his head, skeptical.

She nodded.

"Great."

Star tried to redo the smile she'd given Bobby in the car, but it felt awkward. She bit her lip again — *Bad habit; gotta stop biting my lip* — and she wished her stomach would stop fluttering. She also wished she'd had a few drinks, or taken the pill Lacy had offered her. "What do you want tonight?"

He glanced at the TV, reached for the remote, turned down the volume. "I want everything."

Star gave a genuine grin. It was a relief to think she might spend the entire night with this one guy. Much better than the stories she'd heard from Brandi, who loved to scare the new girls — or so Lacy had said.

"Dance for me."

Star hesitated. She wasn't naturally a great dancer. But the thought came to her, *This is like an audition.* She didn't have any music, though — just the moans and cries escalating behind her.

"Stand in front of the TV," the guy instructed her.

He moved to the edge of the bed. He was a movie director, and this was her chance. Star stared at him; she gave him a bit of a smile. She started playing a song in her head, and started moving to it. She put her hands over her head and turned slowly, then moved her hands down her body as gracefully as she could. There was a mirror on top of the bed. The lights felt too bright.

He was undressing. "Do you like this?" he asked, motioning to himself. Star smiled and bobbed her head, dancing slowly in front of the TV. She tried not to think about that time with her friend Molly, looking at porn for the first time ever, on Molly's computer — laughing till they cried. They both thought penises were the ugliest things they'd ever seen. Star bit her lip again and kept moving slowly to her own silent music. Then music actually started — it came on behind her; she turned in her dance to see that the orgy was picking up energy. Now there were flashing lights and music with a beat. She didn't really know how to dance like this. She and Molly used to work on routines, but none of that stuff seemed to work now. Star kept doing the same few moves she could think of, over and over, hoping it would be all right.

Maybe this wouldn't be so complicated after all, she told herself. She could imagine it was Bobby, just like he had told her. But then it was also Richard Gere — cool. And this was also a movie, and she was playing her part! Awesome!

But then came the impact — and the sting.

It was a second or two before Star realized he had slapped her.

"Did you like that?"

Star was trying to recover, trying to answer. He took her arm and pulled her to the bed.

"Tell me you liked it."

She nodded — but her face stung, her eyes were watering from the blow.

"Tell me, you dirty slut."

"I like it," she gulped.

He slapped her again. "So I'm your first trick, huh?" he asked, grinning widely. "What do you want to do to me?"

Star looked at him, her mind racing. She remembered Lacy's instructions. "Never let a john think you don't want him. It don't matter what he looks like or what he asks for. You smile pretty and make him believe you're enjoying every second with him."

Star smiled, her face tingling with pain. "I want whatever you want."

"But you sluts love this," he sneered. "You want me to do bad things to you, and you want to do nasty things for me."

She tried to look agreeable. But she was really wondering about Bobby. *Is Bobby going to be mad about him slapping me?*

Star was thinking hard. Trying to remember what movie this scene was from. She imagined it was the new version of *Pretty Woman*. She was the lead. This was the part where the leading man would rush in and save her. He'd beat up this guy, wrap her in a blanket, carry her in his arms to safety.

But no hero came. No hero would be coming. Star knew it.

Only this man was coming toward her, his face contorted with lust, and rage—Star was frightened.

You can do this, she told herself. This was the hard training, and she would survive it.

What he did was violent and painful, her cries and moans only made him hurt her more.

It might have been half an hour, that's what Star figured, before he was up again, making a drink and walking around naked. She got up and used the bathroom, while he phoned someone. It stung to pee, and she was bleeding. She wondered if he would keep her all night and do all those things to her again. Maybe she could take a bath now?

She wrapped a fluffy white towel around her — one of the nicest towels she had ever touched before and hesitated before she went back in the room. He was dressed. Did that mean she could get dressed too?

"A few of my buddies want to meet you."

The next part seemed like hours. Finally, someone called from the other room to say that "company" had arrived. Within a few minutes, the cameras and men were gone, and Star was alone.

***

"They should have paid extra!" Bobby was screaming. "Damn, and they filmed it!"

Somehow, it made Star feel better that he was furious.

When the men had finished with her, she didn't think she could walk. Lacy had appeared and wrapped her in a robe and helped her out of the hotel room. "Come on, we gotta get outta here before they be back," Lacy had said tersely, picking up Star's clothes from the floor. "They want us gone, so we gotta be gone."

"How long have you been here?" Star asked, stumbling.

"They ordered more girls, so Bobby sent us over to party."

Star felt confused. Why hadn't she seen Lacy earlier?

"Bobby's going to kill them," Star muttered.

"Why's that?" Lacy asked, a touch of scorn in her voice.

"They, they did things." Star tried not to cry.

"They already paid Bobby," Lacy answered coolly.

Star didn't know what to say to that. Bobby wasn't going to kill them?

At least when they were all together back in their hotel room ... at least when Bobby had heard the whole story ... at least he was angry. He slapped Lacy hard across the face.

"You were there," he growled. "Stupid ho!"

He hit Lacy again, knocking her to the floor.

So Lacy isn't so cocky now, Star thought.

Lacy crawled away from Bobby, holding her face and crying for him to stop.

That's when Cherry stood up, taking a position between Bobby and the stricken Lacy. "She thought *you* made the deal," Cherry said brazenly.

"You think you can protect her," Bobby shrieked, "an old slut like you?" He grabbed Cherry's hair, yanking her head downward as she cried out in pain.

Star curled her legs in helplessly, unable to do anything but watch the scene, hoping no one landed on her.

Bobby was still grasping her hair. Now he grinned an evil grin. "You oughta be glad some guys still like used-up hos like you." He yanked her head lower.

"Bobby! Stop it!" Lacy cried from the floor. "Cherry, please. Just leave it alone. Bobby, please stop. You won't make no money with a bunch of beat-up hos."

He yanked Cherry's head further toward the floor, then let go.

"They'll make a killing on that video," he growled. "We didn't get nothin' for the video."

"I'm sorry, Bobby," Lacy cried. "I didn't know." She was backing into the corner between the bedside table and the wall.

Bobby paced the room as Star curled into a ball on the bed, wincing in pain. He'd promised she would sleep with him; would he remember? She knew better than to ask when the anger had him. He'd be nicer in a few hours.

"I gotta make some calls." He stormed out.

Cherry helped Lacy get up from the corner and sit on the edge of the bed. She held her cheek. Then Cherry began rubbing Star's back, ever so softly, and made soothing sounds, almost like a mother.

Cherry gently moved a strand of Star's hair from her face. "Are you girls okay?" she asked quietly. Star nodded, with her eyes closed. She didn't hear Lacy respond.

"One night, I had 19 tricks," Cherry said. "It was ridiculous." Lacy laughed. Star couldn't believe what she was hearing. Lacy acted like what happened to Cherry was no big deal. Star glanced at Lacy with disgust.

"What?" Lacy responded, glaring at her. "You think you're the first one to go through something like this? Tonight isn't even worth a story. The girls were ordered not to tell you any of their stories yet. But just wait. Did anyone hold a gun to your head?"

Star shook her head. Lacy was obviously just talking crazy. Wasn't she?

"Did they tie you up, knock out any teeth, burn you or stick things in you, cut you, force you to lick their crap off the floor?"

Star shook her head again. Now she realized tears were streaming down her face.

"You don't have to scare the kid half to death," Cherry said, rubbing Star's back a bit harder. "It's okay, sweetie; you've been through a lot tonight."

Star sighed heavily. She was grateful that all the other girls were in other rooms tonight. She was grateful for Cherry. She was an old ho, nearly 30. She had been in this longer than Star had been alive.

But Cherry hadn't said that Lacy was making up the stories. Star's stomach turned. *Are those really things that happen?*

"Then it sounds like you had a pretty decent first night," Cherry said. "Now go take a bath. There's some medicated cream in the cupboard."

Star groaned as she tried to get out of bed. The towel between her legs was bright red with blood, from the front and behind. Her lip was split; her mouth was bitter with blood. But now, she just wanted to get clean. Cherry helped her into the shower. The water stung, but Star scrubbed her skin with the hottest water she could stand. Her flesh turned bright pink as she soaped every inch of her body — twice — except extra-carefully over the sore areas.

Lacy pulled back the shower curtain. "By the way," she said matter-of-factly, "I found the twenty in your shoe. Don't ever hide tip money from Bobby. He'll find out, and he'll beat you for it."

Star opened her mouth to try and explain; the water gurgled into her throat. One of the guys had told her to buy herself something nice with the twenty. He'd put it in her shoe. She thought it could be hers.

But Lacy was gone before she could explain.

Cherry left her some Vicodin. Star took two.

Later, she didn't remember if she slept with Bobby that night or not.

Commentary — What is This Exactly?

"Here?"

My husband and I were sitting outside with friends, at our favorite restaurant overlooking the Columbia River.

"You mean it's going on *here?*"

We hadn't seen our friends in quite some time, and now the subject of my work had come up. They knew I dealt with human trafficking in other countries. But in America?

The look of shock on their faces was the same one I've had myself — not once, but many times — as our research and investigations have taken me across the nation, and I've seen for myself, over and over again, the truth of the sex trafficking industry in the United States.

In coming to terms with the truth, recognizing the technical terms can be helpful.

"Commercial sex," according to Public Law 106-386, occurs when money or something of monetary value (drugs, shelter, food, clothes, etc.) is exchanged for a sex act.

"Sex trafficking" is a component of commercial sex. This is "the recruitment, harboring, obtaining, and transporting of persons by use of force, fraud, or coercion for the purpose of subjecting them to commercial sexual exploitation."

It's "sex trafficking" whenever a human is bought or sold for sexual use and the exchange somehow benefits another person — whether it's the individual herself, or a family member, some outside party, a facilitator, or any party to any form of business arrangement.

According to federal law, the sex trafficking of children occurs when minors (under the age of 18) are sold for sex or a sexually-related activity such as prostitution, stripping or exotic dancing, and/or child pornography.

When we add "domestic" and "minor" to this definition — as in "Domestic Minor Sex Trafficking," or DMST, we're referring to the sex trafficking of children within the borders of the United States of America.

DMST means our kids sold as a sex product within our own country.

"Is it really happening here?" my friend asked at the riverside restaurant.

I thought of the faces that haunt me ... the girls who "live" with me now, throughout my days and nights. I thought of the children being used at that very moment in hotels and truck stops in Portland, Oregon/Vancouver, Washington, the very area where we were meeting.

"No," she wanted me to say, "it's elsewhere. It's happening in poor countries, far away from our comfortable lives. Not here."

We all wanted me to answer that way.

Instead, I had to nod and say, "Yes. It is. Right here."

I hope someday I can answer her differently.

"The stark reality is that the supply is ever-present, right? I mean, that little girl who ended up on the streets of Washington State is way, way, way too typical, right? They're an endless supply, endless supply. And it is almost surreal to have those words leave my mouth — endless supply of victims. But that's the stark reality."

—Andrew Oosterbaan, Department of Justice,
Criminal Division, Chief of the
Child Exploitation and Obscenity Section

(National Training Conference on the Sex Trafficking of America's
Youth, September 15, 2008, sponsored by Shared Hope)

Chapter 4

Organizing Crime

James Lopez in Fort Lauderdale, Florida

Jimmy's eyes searched the children on the playground for the one with a red sweatshirt and black hair. He leaned out the side window of his silver car. He squinted at the group playing four-square. No red sweatshirt anywhere.

Finally, there he was. Lance had taken off his sweatshirt. He was deep into an intense game — that boy played four-square every recess.

Jimmy glanced around to see if anyone else was watching. Then he could relax. He leaned back in his seat with his eyes on the game. He took a sip of his Big Gulp. His cell phone rang.

"Yeah?"

"We need you to come in."

It's my day off, Jimmy wanted to say. But there were no days off for the FBI, not really.

The recess bell rang. Lance turned toward the fence. He waved at Jimmy with a wide smile.

Jimmy laughed out loud, shaking his head. So his son had seen him there after all. He wished he could watch his kid every day. The things he knew, the things he had seen and learned on the job, made Agent James Lopez want to follow Lance from morning to night, to keep him safe.

Jimmy waved back and turned the key. A week earlier, they'd made one of their biggest raids. It stretched from coast to coast. But it wasn't enough. He could take 40 pimps off the street, and 40 more would crop right back up. Too much demand. Demand would keep the business thriving. Yeah, at the moment, they were supposed to be celebrating the great victory of arresting all those pimps. The case was unprecedented in its scope.

So why didn't he feel like celebrating?

Jimmy knew he'd been called in to do more interrogating. To get the evidence that would put bad people away. To lure out the names that would enable more arrests. Maybe it would slow things down out there, save someone's life, set a standard to cut down the crime. That's what his life was about, Jimmy reminded himself.

But he knew what his life was *most* about was, at this moment, racing in toward Mrs. Cushion's second grade classroom. And Jimmy hoped to make that kid's world a whole lot safer.

***

Bobby Bad in Las Vegas

"The Feds are coming after everyone," Krazee said — and then attached a string of profanities.

"Calm down, man," Bobby said. He was tired of these conversations. He'd had enough of small-timers freaking out over the new Innocence Lost bust. Forty arrests across the country wasn't that many, not considering how many pimps were in business in every city in every state.

Sure, it was, Bobby had to admit to himself, a neon warning to every town and cell phone plan in the country. He'd been on the phone for hours. This was bigger than any other case, ever. But in a way, it was cool with Bobby Bad. It reminded him of the old days of pimping, when guys like Iceberg Slim were dogging the law in Chicago.

"Listen, Kraz, we've got businesses to run," Bobby barked into the cell phone. "It's opportunity knocking, that's what it is. We got the big fight next month. With Amazing Jay and Mega out, we need girls. Their clients already been calling me. What happened to their girls?"

"They busted too." Krazee sounded near panic. Bobby shook his head. Guys like this didn't deserve the life. Krazee liked to beat his girls and act all badass, but now he was practically crapping in his pants.

"I'm done, Bobby," Krazee whimpered. "They're shutting us down, and I can't do more time."

Bobby was done with guys like this. He needed to build some better associations. "You want out, man?" he snarled. "What you gonna do?"

"Don't know. But I'm out of town for a while. Going to So-Cal for a while, lay low, visit my mom, see what happens."

"Visit your *mom*." Bobby swore. He had only weeks; he needed another four dozen girls, more if he could get them.

"Hey, man, I got my cousin in Kansas City who can bring in some girls," Krazee offered. "He's close to some brothers too; maybe they can help. Take my girls for a while, you can have 'em straight out."

Bobby could tell: Krazee was hopeless.

Bobby cut off the conversation and immediately dialed Lacy. She always answered him, no matter what.

"Kinda busy right now," she said, her voice smooth as silk. That voice meant she was with a regular, but Bobby didn't call without reason — and she'd make it up to the client.

"Baby, we need to talk."

"Few hours?"

"Get done fast and call me." He wasn't giving her a break on her quota, but Lacy knew how to bring in the dough if she had motivation.

"Sure thing, baby."

"How's Star?" he asked off-handedly. That hot little number could be a nice money-maker, just groom her right.

"Fine, just fine. Working like everybody."

He heard an agitated voice in the background. "Come on, girl!"

Bobby hung up and turned off the ringer on his phone. He needed a moment. He leaned back against the headrest of his prized Mercedes. Lil' Wayne thumped through him from the sound system; he followed the rap tapping his thick ring against the steering wheel.

All those rappers on TV, those posers, making like the pimping life was all glamour and glitz ... they weren't *living* it, that's for sure. It was damn hard work getting those girls to do anything. All they did was bitch and gossip, gossip and bitch some more. Taking care of them was like taking care of a tribe of trashy children. He had to be dictator and boyfriend at the same time.

"It's like being a coach," his old man used to say. "You gotta coach the team, pick the right players for the right position, know how to stack your lineup." Everything with dear old Dad had been about baseball, even his pimping.

Bobby closed his eyes. This was his new Zen-like method of problem-solving. Bobby had bought a few new books on management and the power of focus. The mind works better in a calmed and relaxed state, he had learned. Bobby thought of how his old man would've gotten all into the Zen mind stuff. His father was good — not as good as Bobby Bad, but good. Dad knew how to work the girls, coach the team — Bobby's mother was one of his longtime players. But Bobby knew, now, that it takes even more than Dad's methods. It takes more than a good rousing talk to get the girl to do anything.

What hos needed, Bobby had figured out, was to be reminded — and often — who's boss. Sometimes there was nothin' better than giving a beating and getting all the frustrations out. Then he could think again. He'd also learned to use psychology. Women had basic needs — if they thought he loved them, they'd do anything. Also — he couldn't let them get too close to one another. Couldn't give them any true independence. No accumulation of money. Get them to show you just the perfect balance of love and fear.

Bobby turned down the music and pulled out his Blackberry. Time to work; the Zen break was over. He'd make some calls, then check on the girls. It was up to him to keep the business running.

***

Ricco in Kansas City, Missouri

Ricco tried to keep his voice calm.

"Is this Bobby?" he asked.

He'd been waiting for this call since his cousin's voicemail. This was the kind of break Ricco had been waiting for — but the panic in Krazee's voice held him back.

"I need some girls," Bobby Bad said, sounding casual, "for the fight next month."

"How many?"

Ricco had never been to Sin City, even though one of his girls was from there; she kept calling it the "ultimate vacation playground." Ricco's operation ran fine in Kansas City. Sure, it got cold in the winter, but nothing like the years he'd worked in Alaska. There was only so much snow a man could take. But Vegas? Vegas would be a leap up, in so many ways.

"Twenty or 30?"

Ricco needed to answer quickly, or he wouldn't have another call like this for a long time. But he hesitated. Las Vegas seemed a bit out of his league. He'd heard the stories. The Mexicans, the Russians, the Brothers, the Chinese, Cubans, Colombians, Albanians ... it was a freakin' U.N. summit around there, from what he'd heard. Here in K.C., he had the Brothers — who stuck together; they didn't much like the white guy operating on their street. It was just that Ricco had a few connections, so they left him alone.

Ricco made himself answer. "Whatever you need," he said, trying to relay confidence. He'd need to make a slew of calls for this to happen. But he'd get paid, he knew that, and paid well. "Requests?"

"The usual, with some young."

Ricco grunted in agreement. *The usual.* "I've got some new product. Fresh, very fresh."

"Good. Let's talk soon then."

An hour later, Ricco pulled up to the curb where Kelsey stood with her backpack on her shoulder. She hurried toward the car as Ricco hit the unlock button.

"What do you want to do?" he said as she hopped in the car. "Have you eaten?"

"I'm a little hungry," Kelsey said with a smile. He touched the end of her nose and thought that today he'd kiss her. She'd been eager for it for a while. Some girls, though, he knew it was best to drag along a bit. Anticipation — that's what made the heart grow fonder.

"I bought you something." He grabbed the gift bag from the Escalade's back seat.

"For me?" Kelsey looked ecstatic. The kid probably hadn't been given a gift like this in her entire life. Ricco looked at it as an investment. She opened the little box — a silver bracelet — and squealed with excitement.

"Thank you!" she gushed, putting it on her wrist. "I won't take it off!" Ricco knew she wouldn't.

"So where to? We could see a movie or go to the arcade for a while."

"I can't be out late. My dad was home."

Ricco looked at her closely. "He didn't touch you, did he?"

"No," Kelsey replied, shaking her head, he wouldn't do that. "He just drinks and yells a lot." She turned her wrist over, admiring the jewelry. "I can't blame him. Mom's had three boyfriends since they separated. I'd rather have him back than her boyfriends."

"Did they touch you?"

Kelsey hesitated ever so slightly — and Ricco knew the answer. It was the same, with all of these girls. The story had a different face, but it was always the same story.

"Oh baby, it's going to be okay," Ricco cooed. "I'll take care of you. You want me to talk to your dad? You want me to track down those guys?"

"No!" She shook her head wildly. "It's okay. But I think my mom is going to move in with her sister in Iowa."

"Iowa. You aren't going to Iowa."

"I know, it's terrible. I want to be with you. I don't want to go."

This is going to be easy, Ricco thought. "You can come with me," he said smoothly. "You're mature enough to make your own decisions, aren't you?"

Kelsey nodded.

She was 14, older than a lot of the girls working, and an easy new addition to the stable.

She'll be ready, Ricco said to himself, *just in time for the Vegas trip.*

"I said I'd take care of you, didn't I?"

Commentary — Why Is It In America?

Our team at Shared Hope has spent years examining the worldwide marketplace where women and children are sold for whatever sexual acts the buyer desires.

For one project, we were funded by the U.S. Department of State's "Office to Monitor and Combat Trafficking in Persons." The concept was to choose a sampling of various countries and see what was happening in each specific culture and region of the world. The list of countries ended up being quite diverse: Japan, Jamaica, The Netherlands, and the U.S.

We decided to include the United States in our profile to see just how extensive the global trafficking industry was, and whether girls were being imported into America from other nations, what their average age might be, and how big the demand really was.

I wasn't expecting to uncover the unfathomable. But we did.

At the beginning of the study, I thought the largest number of victims in the USA would be foreign, and the primary buyer would be a man who traveled across national borders to buy sex from a victim. Our investigation proved me painfully wrong.

While the U.S. government was officially committed to spending serious money to fighting trafficking and restoring victims in the U.S., we found that Washington was actually concentrating its resources on the estimated 17,000 to 18,000 men, women, and children brought across the borders *into* America for labor or sex. But *there are over 100,000 domestic child sex trafficking victims in the USA each year* — 100,000 or more who *don't* come in from other countries — are our own children.

In the area of efforts against buyers, our government was focused mainly on Americans who travel overseas to buy foreign children. But our research found that men in any country, our own included, don't usually travel far to buy a trafficked child. In any area where buying sex is "normalized," *local men buy* — unhindered by legal penalty or public shame.

There were common threads that tied all of the countries together:

1. Child sex slavery can only happen in countries, regions, and communities that have developed a culture of tolerance for

commercial sex.

2. Sex tourism has grown with globalization. It's no longer Western men traveling to developing countries to buy sex. It is found worldwide. Local men are buying locally as the sex markets in places like Las Vegas and Amsterdam become normalized, culturally tolerated.

3. Because of stricter immigration laws and heightened terrorist threats internationally, it has become harder to move product (human beings) across the borders. As a result, local abductions and recruitment of innocent children are on the rise.

4. The Internet has created an explosion of pornography use, which is also a marketing tool for sex trafficking — and a potential gateway for the people viewing pornography to become buyers in the sex markets. Child porn is widespread, and video images of younger and younger victims lead buyers to demand younger and younger victims in order to fulfill the fantasies ignited by what they're seeing. The porn depicts children enjoying sexual acts, and buyers want to experience what they've seen.

Our research was exhaustive. Over the course of years, we went inside the sex markets with undercover human rights investigators. We reviewed the undercover footage. We studied the data, we made the charts — and finally produced our assessment. The subtitle was "A Comparative Examination of Sex Tourism and Trafficking in Jamaica, Japan, The Netherlands, and The United States" — but the main title reflected what we had discovered about the "driver" of the entire global industry: *DEMAND.*

What we had discovered was the existence of a dark subculture which not only exists worldwide, but is thriving at an explosive rate in the United States as well. And, sad to say, it is recession-proof.

I'm often asked, Why did this curse fall upon America? Could it be because of this, or that? My answer is always, yes:

- Yes, the Internet and rise in pornography feed the industry.
- Yes, our culture of tolerance facilitates it (more and more).
- Yes, moral ambiguity nurtures its growth.

- Yes, our society — our media, our advertising, our television, our movies, our reality shows — influences the industry and the public's perception of it, with our sexually-oriented culture, with our disappearing boundaries.
- Yes, our laws and law enforcement procedures need a massive overhaul.
- Yes, the most innocent in our society are being victimized.

The sex industry came home to me. I had the statistics and reports and had seen the venues.

And then I began to meet the women. Our American girls.

Chapter 5

Boot Camp

Lacy and Star in Las Vegas, Nevada

Lacy adjusted her skirt as she rose from the car. She flashed her bright smile back at the john behind the wheel. He was waving at her with a grin. She tucked the $10 tip into her bra with the rest of her money. She'd make her $1,000 easy today. With Bobby's business plan to work on, and the grooming of Star, Lacy had some slack in her quota lately.

She checked the time and tried Star's number for the third time. She was getting Star's voicemail again as she walked by Candy — sitting on a curb, crying again. One of Blade's girls. *What kind of guys like picking up a girl covered in bruises?* Lacy wondered. But that was how most of Blade's girls looked, and his business appeared to be doing just fine.

Lacy hung up on Star's voicemail and hurried up the outside stairway to the second floor of the Starlight Motel. When she saw that the door was ajar, Lacy quickened her pace.

The room was empty. In the desk drawer: $100, nothing else. Star had gotten a few days off — after her first night, to heal up — and now the kid seemed to think she got perks the others didn't.

Lacy heard something in the bathroom. The door was locked; she knocked softly.

"What are you doing?" Lacy asked.

"I don't feel good." Star sounded pathetic.

"Who the hell does?"

Lacy shook the door knob and knocked again. "Let me in."

There was a long silence before Lacy heard movement. The lock clicked. Lacy opened the door. Star was settled into a crouch in the bathtub.

There was no water in the tub, but the kid was naked, soaking wet, huddled in a ball shivering.

"What the hell are you doing?" Lacy snarled, though she couldn't help the pangs of sympathy. The girl looked like a tiny drowned mouse, staring up at her with giant blue eyes. Star was about to cry, tears cresting the rims of her eyelids.

Lacy wanted a threat to work: *You cry, and I'll beat you myself.* But that wouldn't work with this one. There was a delicate equilibrium between firmness and sympathy, a balance that took the powers of observation and precise timing to control — that's what Bobby had told her. Still, Lacy wasn't getting control of the feeling that she should wrap Star up in a blanket ... call her mom or dad — if only the kid had a mom or dad to go to.

"He looked just like my dead grandpa."

Star burst into tears and began to shake against the stained porcelain of the tub. Lacy looked around for a towel and found a poor excuse for one folded on a rusting shelf. She took Star's arm and guided her gently up and out of the tub. These kind of sympathetic jobs were better for Cherry or Ginger — not her. Lacy cursed and scolded Star, but softly, as she gently dried the girl's body. There was a bright red bite mark on Star's back. She still had fingertip bruises on her arms from before, and bruises on her legs.

Why any guy would want this scraggly little thing was beyond Lacy. The kid had no hips, no curves whatsoever. Her breasts were just plain pathetic.

"But he wasn't your grandpa, was he?" Lacy said, thinking that "grandpa" must be the lone hundred dollars in the drawer.

"It was so disgusting," Star sobbed. "He didn't even have teeth. And he stuck his tongue in my mouth!" This made her bawl again, and cling to Lacy ferociously.

"I don't want to do this anymore." She sobbed and sobbed as they sat on the bed.

It took nearly an hour for Star to control herself. Just when Lacy thought the kid had it together, she'd fall apart all over again. Lacy tried to be patient, but she had her own quota to finish, and Bobby was going to be mad that two of his girls weren't working the prime hours. It wouldn't be Star who took the heat for it, either.

"Listen, little Miss America, this is the life."

"I didn't think it was going to be so bad, that first night," Star gulped. "That guy was really cute. A movie director and everything. But then all his friends ... It hurt so bad. It still hurts almost as bad."

Lacy had to listen to the whole thing again. This kid had no idea.

"I told you about acting and going somewhere in your mind."

"I'm trying."

Lacy could see the girl wasn't getting it. She sighed.

"I'm going to tell you something. I want you to listen."

Star stared at her and wrapped the bedspread around her shoulders.

"We all hate this part of it," she said. "We've all had it bad. We've all had terrible things happen to us. We all think Bobby loves us best."

Star stiffened.

"We all know that we're just being pimped out, that we're just hos out there."

Lacy could see reality settling in — the horror that they all had to confront, and accept, at some point.

"This is what you've got to do. Listen. You gotta get tough inside. You gotta put on your act on the outside, but inside, you be tough and strong. You don't let anybody take away who you are, you got it?"

"How do I do that?"

"Go deep down when it's tough, when it hurts. Let the pain feel like its somewhere else, that it's not you feeling it. All this takes some practice, but you'll be stronger real soon."

"But Bobby—"

"Listen to Lacy, not Bobby."

Lacy could see that a lot of this was too soon for Star. She didn't have it in her yet to be strong, to understand what it meant to save a piece of herself from all of this. The kid was hooked on Bobby. She wanted to believe he was her Prince Charming. Some things could only be understood through experience. A year from now, this kid wouldn't be recognizable to her own self.

"You're working harder than any actress," Lacy continued, "harder than your Hannah Montana. Harder than those actresses like Kate Winslet and Jessica Beil. You won't have any problem doing the job after all this."

Lacy's phone beeped. She picked it up and texted a message back. Star picked up her panties and bra.

"But this old man today," Star whined, "he was so gross. At least the others weren't so disgusting."

"Did he have money? Did he pay you?"

Star gestured toward the dresser drawer.

"So you got him, didn't you?"

"What do you mean?" She winced as she pulled up her underwear.

Lacy leaned back on the dresser. "Oh these guys think they're getting something from you. But what are they getting? You aren't giving anything of yourself away. Bobby has your whole heart, right? You do a little act, make them feel all sexy about their pathetic selves, help them get off. And then you walk away with their hard-earned cash. Some are old and fat and smelly and gross. You'll meet every kind of guy out there. Most are married. Most are so messed up, they don't even know it. And you know what? Sometimes it'll even feel good. You've got to learn how to make it feel good. Take care of yourself. Bobby will want that."

"But if Bobby isn't there," Star asked, "isn't that like I'm cheating on him, if it feels good?"

Lacy laughed. "Girl, do you feel like Bobby's cheating on you? When he's with all those women?"

Star paused. Lacy knew Bobby had told this kid some story. Probably that he only thought of her, and that he wished he didn't have to sleep with his other whores, something like that. Lacy felt a shot of anger course through her. She could remember the moment he said the very same words to her. But she wasn't going to put this kid in her place just yet.

"You *are* special to him," Lacy went on. "He told me. He really loves you a lot, you know. He said he wants to buy a big house someday."

"That's what he told me too," Star replied, brightening a bit. "That we'll live in a big house, and I can be a singer. He wants to rap too. So we'd both be musicians."

Lacy picked up Star's clothes, tossing them on the bed. She sat on the edge of the dresser, looking down at her own long brown legs.

"So, for now, you gotta do some stuff you don't like," Lacy sighed, "and some old nasty guys. But what would you be doing? You're not out there busting it at some greasy restaurant, making minimum wage working all day and night. We make more in one night than you'd make in most jobs in a month."

Lacy opened a drawer in the dresser. It was littered with condoms, lubricant, a bottle of vodka. She opened the screw top, took a gulp, handed it to Star. "Here baby, take a drink of this."

A few days earlier, Star would have shaken her head. *I don't drink,* she would have said, *I don't do drugs.* Now the girl took a drink, gasped at the burning in her mouth, then took another. Within a month, Lacy knew, she would have to talk to the kid about not becoming a junkie.

"It gets easier, baby, I promise," Lacy assured her. "By next month, it won't be hard. Girls you went to school with are doing this same thing, but you're getting paid for it."

Star thought about that a moment. "But they're not doing the guys I'm doing."

Lacy pulled a red lipstick out of her purse and turned toward the mirror. She applied it as she talked.

"But they aren't living this life, either!" Lacy insisted. "In Las Vegas, with all this opportunity, and the money you're making!"

She didn't remind the girl that it was actually Bobby making the money. No need to mention that ugly little detail — even though, for some reason, that detail had been nagging at her lately, and more and more.

There was a knock at the door. Star looked up, surprised.

"And remember those girls back home," Lacy added, "they're doing it with worse guys. Don't you know all those uncles, dads, stepbrothers, and mothers' boyfriends?"

Star's eyes followed her as Lacy went to the door. "And wouldn't that be worse? Here at least you've got control. You get the money afterwards. You have the power. All these men are weak and pathetic, handing over their money so you can do 'em for a few minutes. Before, you were a victim. Now you're in charge."

She opened the door to a middle-aged guy in a polo shirt and slacks;

he was glancing around nervously. "Come on in, baby."

Star had already hurried into the bathroom.

"Hi," the guy said.

"Here for a convention?" Lacy asked.

He looked surprised at that, worried and paranoid. "I do pharmaceutical sales." He stuttered slightly. "This is in my region." He sat at the edge of the chair. "But, um — I kind of wanted a blonde, though."

"She'll be right out," Lacy said, motioning toward the bathroom. "She's a little shy."

His eyes grew wide. "Good!" There was relief in his voice. "Great."

"You be nice to her, okay?" Lacy said with a twinkle in her eye. Guys like this loved to feel that kind of power. Within a few minutes, Lacy had left the room with Star's payment in her bra. Something about this girl made her heart ache — and also ticked her off. Lacy pitied the kid's ignorance. Star really did think Bobby wanted her over all the rest of them. But Lacy knew how Bobby used this, as his tactic, pitting the girls against one another. She'd been with him long enough to know things about him that Bobby didn't even know. He had this dream, for one thing, to be one of the legendary pimps of Vegas. He wanted to make a lame-assed dad proud — a dad who had been killed robbing a liquor store when his habit got out of control. Lacy knew she was the only one who knew the real Bobby Bad, and she'd made herself invaluable to him, an equal — despite what the rest of them believed. This scrawny kid called Star was no star; she had nothing over what she and Bobby had gone through together.

The sun had dropped behind the bare mountains. The lights of Las Vegas rose to meet the night. The asphalt steamed after the 100-plus degrees of the day. The girls also rose as the evening cooled, rose with the falling of the sun and the waking of the night — their world. It didn't matter their age, or if they wanted to go home, or what they once dreamed of. They were ladies of the night.

And Lacy didn't have long to make little 12-year-old Star one of them.

"None of these women or girls wants to be in this situation of being prostituted or being drug-addicted. You know, their circumstances have gotten them to this point, and those circumstances aren't pretty."
—*Former child sex trafficking victim from Kansas City, Missouri*

Chapter 6

Pimping Lives

Ricco in Kansas City

More girls. He needed more girls.

"You sure you'll get me at least 15?" Bobby was calling to check on the progress. "I'll pay for more."

Ricco promised — though he only had 10 lined up so far. Kelsey would make 11. Then he would need four more, at least.

His nephew was competing at a junior wrestling match that afternoon. Ricco scanned the bleachers. Yeah, there were a few interesting girls. A group of guys, with one girl sitting in the middle of them — then a group of girls, a large group, with two sitting off at one end.

They were all young enough. A number of them were dressed well, overly confident, giving him a look of disdain when he smiled at them. Thirteen or 14 years old — and they could look down on him? Ricco thought about doing something. Have them beg, see them cry — he hated high and mighty girls who looked at him like he was scum. Someday he just might do what he thought of doing. Wipe those smug, upper-middle-class smiles off their faces.

But for now, Ricco would leave them alone. He didn't need the attention you get with frantic parents crying on the evening news.

His nephew Jasper came over and sat beside him. "Got any weed I can buy?"

"Not to buy. I'll give you some."

"Really? Cool, Uncle Ricco."

"You gotta do something for me, though."

The smile on Jasper's face faded.

"Invite some friends over tonight. We'll have a little party at my place.

And I want you to invite some girls."

"Okay, cool." Ricco knew he'd just made his nephew one popular dude among his friends.

"Tell me about those girls."

"What girls?"

Ricco motioned slightly with his head.

"Jackie and that skinny girl? They live in some group home."

Ricco chuckled at that. "Invite them."

"They're freaks."

"Listen. Make sure those two are there. Invite your team. Forget the other girls, though. Do it and I'll get a keg and whatever else you want for Saturday night."

It was too easy really. Ricco was reminded of how much he liked his job. The two girls came to the party at his house, and with the wrestling team all around them, they felt popular for the first time in their lives. Within an hour, the girls were drunk and high. Horny teen guys, fried on drugs, and with the right encouragement, would do exactly what he needed them to do. Jasper helped get the girls into the bedrooms. His nephew didn't think they were freaks anymore, when he took off their clothes. One of the girls had huge boobs. The skinny one that Ricco had led to his bed wore pink panties and bra.

Ricco set up business.

First he called one of the guys to follow him.

"You gotta see this." He peeked around the corner, then drew back and motioned for the guy to look in. Jasper was already having sex with Big Boobs. Then Ricco showed him the thin girl in Ricco's own room.

"Want a turn?"

The kid was scared. Maybe even a 17-year-old virgin. The girl was drunk but still conscious.

"Go talk to her and see what happens. I saw her eyeing you earlier in the night. She wants you."

The kid still didn't step forward, just stared and shifted, wanting it.

"What are you, playing for the other team? Ah, that's why you like wrestling them sweaty boys."

That moved the kid. Ricco closed the door behind him. Then he headed into the living room to the other boys. He'd get them into the bedroom either as a team or one at a time. Ricco had all night.

"We have a cover charge, boys. But lots of amenities. Just 20 bucks."

"Cover charge?" a kid asked.

"Twenty bucks. Didn't Jasper tell you? It helps cover expenses. Come see what we've got going on in the bedrooms."

The twenties came out. Two guys only had a ten, but Ricco was generous. By the time the guys had left or passed out, Ricco had gotten five or six guys to take a turn in one or both of the rooms.

The next morning, Ricco woke to one of the girls crying. She was trying to wake up the other girl.

"Try this; it'll help with the hangover." Ricco handed Big Boobs a bong. It would be her first taste of rock. She'd be an addict by the end of the week. Nothing Ricco hated worse than a junkie whore — they were unreliable, and quickly turned ugly and desperate. But these girls weren't his. He had a number to fill for Bobby, and he'd made a promise.

"I want to go home," Big Boobs said, pushing away the bong.

"Home, what home? You don't have a home."

The second girl was awake now, looking around for her clothing. He almost laughed as she tried to hide her shapeless figure. The first girl was dressed, sitting on the edge of the bed, spinning out from the drug already. "Come on, Carrie," she said. "Let's get out of here."

"You've got a new home here with me."

"What's he talking about?" Carrie said. *Carrie?* Ricco said to himself. He liked "Scrawny" better for her. Her face and body reminded him of a scrawny little rat. He'd give them street names later; but for right now, he'd call them whatever he liked.

"I have a new life for you," he said with a smile, "and a new job."

Big Boobs stared silently at him. Scrawny was picking up speed, trying to hide herself from him. He set the bong down.

"Listen," Ricco went on, calm but threatening. "You aren't leaving." Scrawny sat down beside Big Boobs and started shaking. He gave them a cold stare. "Don't you think I know where you live? You think you can run away? What will you do?"

Big Boobs grabbed Scrawny's hand as the tears began.

"Do you know what happens to hos?"

Big Boobs was shaking her head. "We're not hos."

"No? What do you think you were last night? Go back to school Monday and find out which of those guys you screwed are your boyfriends. You screwed half the wrestling team. You should've seen the cell phone flashes going last night." He laughed at that. Scrawny was shaking her head like a crazy person.

"They paid for you. You made $300, girls. I have it here for you." He held up the money. "But you know what that means. The police won't help you. They arrest hos. Your rich little friends won't ever talk to you again. You probably screwed their boyfriends last night. And if you do go home, what then? The group home can't have hookers there — you might infect the other girls."

It was sinking in now.

"Listen. You can stay with me," Ricco said, switching to a warmer tone. "I'll give you a better life than this crappy town. You'll get to see the world. And you two can stay together."

Scrawny was still crying. Big Boobs glanced around the room. That he had money was obvious everywhere — in the expensive rugs, the black furniture, the stereo system. Such were the advantages of having a home base. He could impress when he needed to.

"Why don't you just rest a while and talk?" he offered. "I have a really good opportunity to offer you two. I'll make you ladies some breakfast, and then we can talk about Las Vegas." He started out, then turned back. "Oh," he said, extending his hand, "and here's your money."

***

Star in Las Vegas

Star held the magazine open and stared at the picture. *I really look like a model.*

"Didn't I promise you?" Bobby said. "You're on your way, kid." He leaned over to where she sat on the edge of the motel bed. "More of that to come." He rubbed her head and walked out the motel door.

Cherry and Kiki were stretched out on the bed, flipping through the pages of another copy of the magazine.

"You look so good, girl," Kiki said. "Bobby had me in an all-Asian rag once, but this is high-classed."

In the photograph, Star looked years older. She looked like someone famous. The magazine was in stands all over the city. They were free — so tons of people would see her. She wasn't a black-and-white image. Hers was a real magazine — color and glossy. Bobby said she was a *hot commodity.*

Lacy was in the adjoining room. She hadn't even looked. A waste of money, she'd told Bobby, a huge expense. Lacy had never been in the magazine.

Star had to admit that the photo shoot had been humiliating. She was completely nude — so many men in the room — and the photographer was a greasy looking guy she had to do in the back room when it was over. In the shoot, first she had to move around in a lot of very exposing positions. It was easier when Bobby joined the shoot, but she still didn't like having to do a lot of those nasty things in front of all those men. But at least it was Bobby, she told herself; and that night, he'd let her sleep all night with him. He'd even allowed her to "spoon" up against his back for a while. And Bobby said he wished they could be like that every night.

"I remember being that young," Cherry said with a sigh. "That was a long time ago."

Star couldn't stop staring at the picture. It was almost good enough for *Maxim* or *Playboy* or the other magazines that Bobby gave her to help her practice her poses. The picture showed her sitting turned to the side. Her head was tilted up with her mouth slightly open. A little image covered her breasts and read, "Barely legal!"

Star looked down at her breasts, imagining them bigger. A lot of the older girls had implants; some of them were huge. Star's boobs looked so small compared to the others — but they looked good in the picture, so maybe for now they were fine. Brandi had said she was way too young for implants. Not even the back alley places they went to would do them till she was at least 15. She needed to be patient.

"Those boobs will start sprouting in another year or two," Brandi told her every time she caught Star looking at them in the mirror.

Star thought of Grandma Doris back home in Nebraska. Grandma would have a heart attack on the spot if she ever saw this. Her friends in school would be horrified — and jealous. The guys would all want her — she'd have more guys than she'd know what to do with. That would be a change. Star wondered if she could put the picture up on MySpace. Or maybe the magazine had a website. Star thought about forwarding it from Cherry's account to some of her old friends in Nebraska. They'd finally see that she'd gotten out of that crappy town. She was working toward the dream. She already looked like an actress.

Star hopped up from the bed. "I'm going to go show Brandi," she said brightly.

"She's working," Kiki called after her, but Star thought she'd see if she was around anyway.

And then, as she walked toward the stairs, she heard the crying. It was coming from inside a room with an open door. Star peered in; there was one of Blade's girls, sitting on the bed. Star paused, then looked up and down the corridor. She wasn't supposed to talk to other girls.

"Are you okay?"

The girl wiped away some tears and nodded.

"You're Candy, right?"

Another nod as Star took a step inside the door. She saw bright red marks on Candy's neck.

"What happened?"

Candy started crying again. Star was too afraid to go further into the room. She knew what had happened. The girls often talked about how violent Blade was with his hos, especially this one. Star couldn't imagine what she'd do if she was with a guy like that. She looked Candy over. The girl was scrawny, with blonde scraggly hair. Bobby would never find her attractive, Star knew that — so maybe she'd be a good addition for Bobby. He was planning to grow the stable, or so Lacy said.

"You know, Bobby's really nice," Star suggested. "He hardly ever beats us. Maybe you should trade up."

Candy shook her head. "Blade. He'd kill me."

"Looks like he might anyway."

Candy pulled her legs in close to her. "You better go. He was coming right back."

Star hesitated, then said good-bye.

***

Lacy and Cherry

They sat at the plastic table with McFlurry shakes in hand. Lacy took a sip, trying to figure out how to convince Cherry.

"You just need to drop it," Cherry said, taking the lid off her cup.

"You're the one who told me to always get tested, no matter what."

"That was a long time ago." Cherry spooned a bit of Oreo shake into her mouth. "The thing is, I already know I've got HIV."

Lacy nearly knocked over her cup. "What? How do you know?"

"Sometimes you just know these things," Cherry said with a shrug.

A woman and two children walked by: one child was crying, another tugged on his mother's shirtsleeve, pleading to go to the playground. Across from them, Lacy looked at a washed-out old man sitting bent over steaming coffee and a hamburger, idly lining up pennies and dimes on the table. Cherry was the closest thing to a mother or big sister that Lacy had known in the past five years.

Cherry shook Lacy's arm. "Aw, don't make that face and ruin our secret McDonald's escape."

"They've got drugs now," Lacy said in sober tones. "Keeps AIDS away for decades."

Cherry laughed. "Why the hell would I want to live for decades, in this life?"

"You want to die like Belle?" Lacy demanded. She pushed her milkshake away. They'd watched Belle deteriorate fast. She started taking meth to get through it. One day she overdosed herself, to escape the suffering. Cherry had found her.

"You're talking to *me* here, Lacy. I *am* going to die like Belle. It might not be AIDS, but it'll be something like that." Cherry poked with the spoon in the cup. "We're all going out like that. You don't see little ol' *former hookers* like us playing bridge at the old folks' home."

Lacy couldn't respond to that. She'd spent half her morning with Star — who believed she'd be like Britney Spears some day — and now she had Cherry looking at life like it was already over.

"I just hope to take some johns with me," Cherry added, grim-faced. "They wanna go without a rubber, more power to 'em. They wanna screw around on their sweet marriages, I'll give them a big fat reminder of their time with Cherry."

Lacy's throat went a little dry. "They'll go home and infect their wives."

Cherry shrugged. "Not my problem. Not my fault."

Lacy closed her eyes a moment. She got tested every six months. She always tried to use a condom, though a number of tricks wouldn't go for it. It was Cherry who had taught her all the ways to survive.

But something had changed in her. Ever since Belle.

"Where's little Miss America?" Cherry asked. It was just like her, dodging away from a difficult subject.

Lacy shrugged. "Bobby's got her on another 'photo shoot,' as Star calls them. She doesn't know the dough Bobby's making on her with his new cyber porn sites. Today they were shooting 'a party.'"

Cherry knew. Bobby and his pimp pals liked to "party." The girls had all taken turns, but Star acted like she was the first. It annoyed Lacy, but she also knew it wouldn't be long before the kid faced the reality of her position. Bobby needed her the least of all his girls.

"You better watch out for that one. She's ambitious."

Lacy nodded. "She just thinks she's in love. It'll kill her one day."

Cherry snorted. "Yeah, just like the rest of us."

Commentary — How Children Get Abducted

From the streets of Las Vegas, a bus station in Detroit, to a 7-Eleven in Eugene and a shelter for hurricane victims in Louisiana ... all across the country, there are people watching and waiting for the unsuspecting and vulnerable. If this seems far-fetched, if this seems paranoid, I understand. But our extensive investigations have documented it. There is no longer any way to doubt the truth. It's happening in America. And the system connects around the world. There is a demand and they will supply.

Their product is named Cassie and Shelly, and on occasion Steve, and thousands of other names and faces that disappear into the darkness. They disappear to us, but somewhere they are living and suffering, longing to escape before they finally adapt to the world they exist in, resigning themselves to a living death.

Usually, a newly-acquired victim is shipped to another city, although occasionally they actually remain in their hometown. We've found that few American girls have ever been sent to a foreign country; also, fewer and fewer foreign girls are being shipped into the U.S. It's simply cheaper to "produce" domestically — commercial sex turns out to be one of the few U.S. products produced cheaply.

There are small-time pimps and hustlers. And there are large prostitution rings, organized, systematic, and powerful.

But large or small, they all know what to do. They've created a system that includes these elements:

1. *Targets* — Though any girl can become a target, there is generally a certain "profile" driving selection. Pimps find it easiest to manipulate vulnerable girls with low self-esteem, girls from troubled homes, foster children, runaways, and sometimes the mentally disabled.

2. *Courtship* — The pimp will introduce himself and gradually get to know a girl. He will listen to her problems and act like he cares. He may shower her with gifts and compliments. Perhaps he'll provide her with food and a place to sleep at night. However, he'll always establish himself as the victim's "boyfriend," creating a

sense of protection and security. This period can last anywhere from a few days to several months.

3. *Isolation* — As the pimp listens to the youth's "troubles" at home or school, and as he is establishing himself as her savior, the pimp also works to isolate the child from those who may object to their relationship. The strategic removal of friends and family members ensures, as the relationship shifts from caring to exploitative, that the child will have no one to turn to other than the pimp.

4. *Transition* — Eventually (after days or months, depending on the unique dynamics of the specific relationship), the pimp will introduce the idea of prostitution. He may say:
   a. "We really need the money."
   b. "You owe me for everything I've done for you."
   c. "It will only be this one time."
   d. "If you love me you'll do it for me."

Or the pimp may immediately use physical violence once he's gained the victim's trust.

It is crucial to recognize, however, that ANY child can become a victim of domestic minor sex trafficking; the strategies described here are only the most common examples of how recruitment takes place.

5. *Control* — The pimp's primary focus is control: controlling every movement the girls make and every dollar they bring in. The physical control is easier to identify and observe; the psychological abuse can be more difficult to understand. A girl who is frequently beaten, cut, raped, and tortured is guaranteed to do everything the pimp wants her to do. Many victims have telltale marks — bruises, scars, tattoos — of the physical violence they endure.

A pimp typically, however, uses a mixture of love and affection with anger and violence. He's quick to fluctuate between the two states. He may tell one of his girls he loves her and in the next minute slap her across the face. This creates a powerful combination of love and fear that makes the victim obedient.

***

From *The Pimp Game: An Instructional Manual*, describing the grooming/breaking process:

> You'll start to dress her[,] think for her, own her. If you and your victim are sexually active, slow it down. After sex, take her shopping for one item. Hair and/or nails is fine. She'll develop a feeling of accomplishment. This shopping after a month will be replaced with cash. The love making turns into raw sex. She'll start to crave the intimacy and be willing to get back into your good graces. After you have broken her spirit, she has no sense of self value. Now pimp, put a price tag on the item you've manufactured.

"I met this guy and he said he was going to take care of me."
—*Former child sex trafficking victim from Atlanta, Georgia*

Chapter 7

What Happens in Vegas, or Atlanta, or Kansas City, or...

Rick from Boulder, Colorado, in Las Vegas

Tyler was following Rick toward the bar.

"My wife asked me what we're doing tonight."

They sat on bar stools. Rick laughed. He remembered the days when he worried that his wife — whichever one he was married to at the time — might have some super-intuition that could see what he was doing away from home. It was easier now; wife #3 didn't ask much, or even want a phone call when he was gone on business trips.

"What did you tell her?"

Rick noticed Tyler fiddling with a napkin. But he knew the guilt would disappear after a few drinks. When the cute waitress came around, Rick ordered two beers and two shots of Jim Beam to get them started.

"I said we were meeting some suppliers over dinner, then playing cards."

Rick tipped the girl five, which got him a nice smile. "Is she one who'll call all night?"

"If she didn't have the baby, probably. But now she's out by 10:30. Every single night."

Rick grunted. He had already heard all about how Tyler's wife had changed after the baby was born. They didn't have sex as often. She didn't take a shower till he came home from work. Blah, blah, blah.

Rick threw back a shot. "We'll head over to The Satin Lounge in an hour. Then we'll go from there. I've got a few favorite girls; I'll introduce you."

Tyler was trying not to look eager, Rick could tell. But eager wasn't enough. Once, Rick had gone out on the town with a guy whose wife called every half hour, and the idiot actually answered. The guy spent most of the night on the phone in bathroom stalls and alleyways. Rick wasn't going to let that happen again.

"Hey, you love your wife and baby. This has nothing to do with the home life. Getting some time to blow off steam makes us better husbands and fathers in the real world. We deserve a bit of a reward once in a while."

"Darn right we do," Tyler said, and downed his shot.

"So why don't you *accidentally* leave your phone in the room before our very important business meeting? Just in case wifey calls?"

Tyler hopped up. "Yeah. I'll be right back."

An hour later, Rick couldn't stop laughing at Tyler. The look on the guy's face was classic "kid in a candy store." It was all Tyler could do to restrain from grabbing the dancers right then and there. Rick thought about slipping one of them some bills to get the guy more than a lap dance in one of the private VIP rooms, but then he decided not to risk it. They had all night.

Tyler handed a 10 to a voluptuous, topless brunette. As she finished her lap dance, she leaned in close, her lips only inches from his face. Then she moved away, tossing back an amazing smile. The poor guy was near heart failure already.

"Ready to go back to your room and call your wife?" Rick chuckled.

Tyler shook his head. "I think I've found heaven."

"That's my boy. Now — you ready to get something real? Or do you want to whack off in the bathroom all night?"

Tyler's eyes were glassy, his face red.

"I want the real thing."

***

Lacy in Las Vegas

What do you want me to do, baby?

Lacy typed the words on the computer, a few letters at a time, between taking the flat iron to her hair.

"Girls!" Lacy yelled. "Hurry up!"

"Lacy gets grouchy when she's multi-tasking," Kiki sang as she smoothed her sleek black curls. "Be sure you don't actually type *hurry up* to the guy you're online with!"

That made the girls laugh; even Lacy couldn't resist a smile. Bobby had launched his new cybersex online chatroom, and she was the fastest typist in the group even if she could only type using her two index fingers.

"It's a convention weekend," Lacy announced, annoyed, as if everybody didn't already know. She was exasperated at Bobby for adding this job to her list. And the girls weren't getting ready fast enough. They should already be on the street.

"I thought there was a convention every week," Star said. She took her hair out of sponge curlers she'd been wearing all day. They bounced up into tight blonde curls.

"Adorable," Cherry said, touching her hair. "You look like Shirley Temple."

"Hurry up, Star," Lacy growled. "Every week there *is* a convention — but a convention *weekend* means there's more than usual. Business should be pouring in — but all of you are still here!"

Lacy's phone buzzed. She hesitated. If Bobby knew they were here, he'd smack her around for sure. "I gotta go. Someone take over for me. Cherry, get the girls out. Except for Brandi — Brandi, get over here."

Brandi didn't move from the bed, where she was staring blankly at an old romantic comedy on TV. Since her latest abortion, her periods were a time of mourning they all suffered through. She was depressed, and nothing — not even a beating from Bobby — was snapping her out of it. Bobby was fuming about another girl being off the track. He had threatened that they'd all start working on their periods if they didn't make up for Brandi's missing quota.

"Brandi," Lacy barked. "Get out of bed and get your back side over here!" Lacy needed her — depressed or not.

Brandi stirred slowly. "I don't know nothin' 'bout computers."

"All you have to do is type the usual nasty crap. And I seen your MySpace page. I know you can use a computer a little bit."

Brandi sighed and rose. "Star set that up for me. I don't know very much. And I'm the worst speller in the world."

"These people aren't looking for a college vocabulary," Lacy snarled. She put on her lipstick and checked her black straightened hair for wayward strands. "The rest of you, get out on the street. Now!"

***

Rick and Tyler in Vegas

"Can I get a black one?" Tyler asked. Then he enunciated: "An Af-ri-can A-mer-i-can." He laughed hysterically and leaned against the glass of the cab window. It was time to cut the guy off the alcohol if they were going to make it all night.

They were riding from one gentlemen's club to another. Rick was about to ask the cabbie where to get some girls for the night when Tyler yelled. "I saw those fountains! In the movie! *Ocean's Eleven*!"

"Yes, you did," Rick sighed.

"That's so cool. Hey, let's stop and walk around here. Taxi guy, stop right here!"

"What the hell, man?" Rick cried. The driver shot a questioning glance at Rick in the rearview mirror.

"Let's get out here!" Tyler shouted, his face to the glass. "Come on!"

"Okay."

Why not, Rick thought. It wasn't even midnight. The taxi pulled to a stop and they made a quick exit. The street was busy with pedestrians walking the Strip, taking in the sights, a few staggering, others laughing. It was one big party down here.

Rick gestured toward the Harrah's sign. "Let's cross," he said. He liked Harrah's outdoor bar, the bartenders who did tricks with the bottles and glasses. Tyler would get a kick out of that. And it might make him stop *talking*.

"I had this major crush on an African-American girl in high school," he said, "and I always wondered what it would've been like to, you know."

"Oh yeah, I know. Believe me, I know." Rick laughed. The kid cracked him up, that was for sure.

A group of women walked by — dressed to kill. Rick smiled at one who held his gaze as they passed. They were walking toward the open-aired stage where people were dancing in front of the band. Rick heard a familiar '80s rock song growing louder as they approached.

"Wow, take a look at them," Tyler said, nudging Rick and staring at the women. "That one liked you."

Rick nodded and moved toward the crowded curved bar. A few blackjack and poker tables were set up along the edge of the bar area.

"We could save money and just go for those girls," Tyler said.

Rick shook his head. "You don't save money on those girls."

"Why? Are they—?" Tyler stopped and looked at the people around him. Rick had given Tyler a crash course in Vegas etiquette. Sure, people think gambling and prostitution are legal in Sin City, he had explained; but in reality, only gambling is legal in the city limits. Prostitution is allowed, practically speaking; it's an integral part of the city's revenue, of that Rick was sure. But legal prostitution ranches are outside the city limits.

"Let's play a few hands," Rick said, moving toward a table with a view of the dance floor. "Those are just bored women looking for some easy fun. We could provide that, yes. But let me tell you from experience, those women will cost you way more in the end."

Tyler wore the same confused expression Rick had been seeing all night. The kid sat beside him and watched as Rick laid a 50 on the table for him, and the dealer passed Tyler a short pile of chips in return.

"You don't walk away from women like that," Rick explained. "They have husbands who come after you, or they want to keep in touch. That's where my wife #3 came from. I met her at a sales conference. Thought it was an easy one-night stand. She cost me child support and alimony from the old wife for the next five years. And then she has an addiction for shoes."

"Ah, I see." Tyler replied.

Tyler had lost his 50 within five minutes. Rick walked away plus-40.

They were moving back toward the street. "So we'll get a black girl and what else?" He felt ready to get on with the real entertainment of the evening.

"Uh, I don't know. What do you want?"

"I'm ordering for you, man. What do you want?"

Confused expression again — Rick wondered if the guy could be as dumb as he acted. "You might as well go all the way. I'll take one for a while, then leave them both to you."

"Both?" Tyler's eyes widened. The kid looked like he'd just envisioned the Promised Land. "Then how about a blonde?"

Rick grabbed a free magazine from a newsstand by the street. They had already seen a number of solicitors along the Strip, guys passing out cards advertising available girls. Tyler had taken every one offered, and joked that he'd need to hide them before his wife unpacked his suitcase.

"What about this blonde?" Rick showed the page to Tyler. The girl had porcelain skin and blue eyes. She was flawless, with a seductive mouth.

"She looks young — too young for me."

Rick nodded but kept his eyes on the page. This one was probably younger than Tyler could guess, he thought, though they had dressed her up to look older.

Tyler pointed to a blonde who looked like a porn star. Fake everything. "I want that one."

"She'll be expensive."

"If the wife complains, I'll say those dinners out are pricey in Vegas. Do you think I can write it off as a business expense?"

They both laughed at that one.

***

Lacy

Lacy was expecting the worst from Bobby. She thought of what to say that might calm him. She'd been trying different tactics. Some worked, others didn't. Last year, right after her 16th birthday, she'd been in the hospital for two days with one of his beatings. He made her work extra almost a year to pay off the hospital bill. Sometimes Lacy let herself imagine leaving Bobby, but she'd been with him since she was Star's age. She'd once believed he loved her like no other too. Now she knew better — but where else would she go? What kind of life could she live? At least she was a bottom ho; that was something.

Then she saw him. She was surprised to find him kicking it with a few other guys next to his new Lexus.

"You're damn lucky there's a special request for dark meat tonight," Bobby sneered at her. The guys laughed as Lacy looked at the address in the text on Bobby's phone.

She didn't waste any time getting out of there. She hailed a taxi and was at the hotel in minutes. She used a side entrance. The room was easy to find — on the lowest level. A typical, basic hotel room.

"Hey, someone looking to party 'round here?" Lacy asked in her sugar tone. There were two guys in the room. She'd done this before, but it usually got rougher than she liked — and it was a helluva lot of work. She'd charge triple.

"He does," said the guy who had opened the door, "don't you, Tyler?"

"Well, hello, Tyler," Lacy murmured.

Tyler jumped up from the desk, reached out and — Rick couldn't believe what he was seeing — actually shook her hand. "Hello," he said, so politely that both Lacy and the other guy laughed.

Lacy sized him up. Tyler was nervous, married, and eager. This would be pretty easy. And his guilt would make him tip her well. Lacy knew this kind of guy. She knew the other guy's type too, and she was glad she wasn't there for him. He had that way of experience about him, and men with experience usually needed more and more. More violence, younger girls, S&M, a dominatrix — something to keep it exciting. The same was never enough.

There was another knock on the door. Lacy stiffened. If another guy walked in, she'd be getting out first chance she got. But it was a girl, someone she'd never seen before — looked like a Pamela Anderson wannabe.

"Hi," the woman said loudly. "Oh, it's a party!"

"I'm treating him to his first threesome," the experienced guy said. But first, you'll come with me." Lacy and the woman glanced at each other and mutually smiled, as if they couldn't wait. The men liked it.

But Lacy didn't like doing hos she didn't know.

The experienced guy took the blonde's hand and they exited, leaving Lacy alone with Tyler.

She sat on the bed and smiled at him.

"So, you have a thing for black girls. Is that right?"

***

Tyler and Lacy in Vegas

Tyler couldn't believe he was actually doing this. This was real, this was actually happening right now. He watched the woman on the bed. It was mind-boggling that this was happening to him. He reached out and touched her smooth dark skin. She took off her clothes slowly, and he felt the excitement burning through him, a new surge with every piece of clothing.

"You're so beautiful," he heard himself say. And she was. Lacy was the sexiest woman he'd ever been in the same room with. She'd asked him what he wanted and told him that Rick had paid for whatever he wished, and for the entire night. The other girl would be there in an hour.

Tyler was perched on the edge of the bed. And his mouth started moving.

"I had a crush on a black girl in high school. She wouldn't give me the time of day. My father would've come unglued anyway. Dad was one of the last racists in town."

The girl stretched out on the bed beside him, listening to his story. His eyes couldn't stop moving up and down the length of her body.

"I didn't, uh, mean any offense with that." He was stumbling over his words. He should just stop talking and start enjoying this. But he was dazed; it still didn't seem real to him.

A cell phone rang. He realized it was his — he grabbed it up and nearly turned it on by accident. He looked; it was Janey. He turned off the ringer and put the phone in a drawer.

A few minutes later, the room phone rang. The girl smiled as Tyler bumbled around, trying to figure out how to unplug it.

"The wife?" Lacy asked in a teasing tone.

"Uh," he began. He nearly denied it. He'd taken off his ring. But Tyler guessed this girl could tell. "That obvious?"

"The good ones are always taken."

He laughed.

"You're different than the others, I can tell." She smiled sweetly, and for a moment, Tyler pictured a life with this woman. Waking up and having coffee together, going to a ball game, doing all those things Janey hated to do — going off to her women's book clubs and save-the-planet meetings.

"So do I give you a tip?" Tyler asked helplessly. "This is the first time I've done this."

Lacy grabbed hold of his pant loops and pulled him onto the bed and toward her. An instant electric shock coursed throughout his body, and within a moment he forgot all about home, work, Janey, the baby, and everything else.

She liked it too. Tyler could tell. He wasn't just another cheating husband to her. She really understood him.

"Whatever you want from me, baby."

Her voice made him instant ready. "Say 'baby' again."

"Don't fall in love with me now," she teased with a wide smile.

Commentary — How Does It Happen?

"They like what they do."
"They don't want to work real jobs. They make so much more money."
"They chose it."
"They could leave it if they wanted to."
"There are places they can go for help."

These are some of the many comments I hear concerning prostituted women. But according to the U.S. Department of Justice, the average age of entry into prostitution is 12 to 14[2] — and a child this young is ill-equipped to make adult decisions.

Certainly many of the girls I've met *believe* they chose the life of a prostitute, though in some cases they started at 11 or 12 years of age. They insist they made their own choice, although it's clear they were actually not choosing to be used, sold, and abused. They say it was their decision to exist in this world — yet clearly it's a world where they've been gang-raped, sodomized, repeatedly beaten, raped with objects, threatened, strangled, tortured, dehumanized, burned with cigarettes, videotaped, humiliated.

If the girls themselves believe they chose it, then how is it not a choice? How does it happen?

The answer lies in the data we've gathered about the main points of entry into "the life." These victims are generally profiled as:

1.   Children kidnapped by a trafficker/pimp and controlled with physical force (beatings, change in locations, physical threats against them and their families, etc.).

2.   Children lured by a trafficker/pimp via the pretense of love and affection and via false promises (they'll be taken care of, they'll have a better life, they will be loved).

3.   Children sold by a trafficker (this includes such cases as a mother trading her daughter for rent or drugs, etc.).

4.   Children who see trading sex as their only means of survival

---

[2]   U.S. Department of Justice — Child Exploitation and Obscenity Section. http://www.usdoj.gov/criminal/ceos/prostitution.html. Accessed on March 11, 2008.

(for food, shelter, safety, or transportation); these children are often targeted by sexual predators who take advantage of their vulnerable situations.

A child in any of these situations is not actually "choosing" to be prostituted.

I remember "Michelle" telling me about being locked in a closet naked, bound by her thumbs and standing on her tiptoes, for two days. She was left there alone except for occasions when her pimp mocked and taunted her from the closed door. He told her she was nothing, dirt, worthless, and that no one cared about her but him. No one cared to save her. No one could save her. She was given no food or water and had to urinate on herself.

In her years on the streets of Seattle, Kansas City, Denver, Anchorage, and elsewhere, Michelle was at various times shot, beaten, tortured, forced to eat feces, dehumanized by taunts and sex, and arrested dozens of times (many times while still a minor) — while her pimps and the men who bought her were rarely, if ever, arrested (and not a single one was ever sentenced).

And Michelle's is not an isolated story. Every girl on the street will encounter violence at one time or another, from the usual rape and torture in the first 24 hours under a pimp's control and repeatedly over the course of the months and years. Violence is essentially part of the job description.

"I needed what I felt was being offered to me," Michelle told me, "which was protection, someone to care for me, someone that cared if I got hurt or if anything happened to me, which of course was all lies. I just wanted someone to care. And so I got pulled into that. The men that I ran across that wanted to help me just wanted to use me."

Michelle was 12 years old when she first traded sexual acts to truckers in return for food, safety, and transportation away from her sexually abusive home. She was introduced to prostitution by that first trucker: he offered to do something for her "if she did something for him." When he was done with her, he passed her to other truckers.

"I don't remember one of them not wanting something in return for a ride or some food," Michelle says today. "One guy took me into a diner because I was really hungry, and I thought he would help me. But in the end, he just used me like the rest."

At one point, she tried to escape her situation, slipping into a phone booth unnoticed. "I just stepped in there to use the phone," she remembers — "and *I had no one to call*. And that was really, really ... that feeling was overwhelming. I just stood there knowing *I had no one to call*."

Tanya from Toledo, Ohio: "Who was there to stop it?" she asked. "Nobody was there to stop it."

And those who believe the women chose prostitution for the money are completely mistaken. As Tanya went on to point out, the girls almost never get money other than what their pimp or madam gives to them. All of their earnings and tips go straight to the pimp — under penalty of more violence.

"It's amazing to hear myself say that," Tanya says. "Like, you think, 'How could you put yourself out there...? Allow men to entice your body for a price and then, everything that you just did that for, you hand it [the money] to another man?'"

But you do what you must to survive — or you die.

Chapter 8

Tears and Lust

Leo in Kansas City

Leo sat in the master bedroom of his mother's home. He was 44 years old but felt 400.

"You aren't alone," people told Leo as they came and went, like it was a funeral.

"Don't give up, and don't lose hope. God is bigger than all of this." That's what his old pastor had said, and Leo wanted to slug him in the face. But he didn't have the energy or the will to do anything, other than allow the downward spiral that his life had become.

The encouraging words were about to kill him. He knew the statistics. He'd heard them on TV crime shows, read them in the novels he loved — Clancy and Baldacci. Every day without word from Millie decreased his chances of finding his baby — or at least finding her alive.

Leo sat watching home videos in the guest room of his mother's house. He'd been back for a week-and-a-half already. The police classified Millie as a runaway; they wouldn't help much. But Leo was doing everything he could.

Tonight, he just needed to see his little girl.

Millie's first day of kindergarten. He'd taken the day off. She wore the white dress with pink hearts, white tights, and patent leather shoes. Karen had said Millie looked ready for Easter, not school.

"Bye, Daddy. I love you, Daddy."

Weren't kids supposed to cry when they went to kindergarten? Not Millie. She was brave. She was eager to show Mrs. Smith that she could already read a few words.

The video dissolved to Millie racing to wrap her arms around his legs. She was holding a picture of herself.

"Hi, Daddy, hi! See what I drew in kindergarten? I go to big school now!"

She couldn't stop chattering about all the things she'd done that day.

Leo's cell phone rang; he pushed *pause* on the remote. He looked at the number and sighed. Every call was hope, and every hope was dashed. The ringing stopped. He started rewinding to watch that part again. Then the phone was ringing again, with the same number.

"What?" he said angrily into the phone.

"Leo, don't ignore me. I feel so alone." The words were sloshy. "I can't believe our little girl is gone."

She'd been drinking again. He swallowed the words he wanted to say, the ones he'd yelled at her the first few days, about her not watching their daughter. But the futility of it filled him. Millie was gone, and yelling at his soon-to-be ex-wife wouldn't help. He'd failed her. He'd failed his little girl. He should have brought her with him when he took the job in Milwaukee. He didn't want to work away from her. But there was no choice. Not in this economy.

Leo thought he'd be back in six months, a year tops. No need to fight it out in the courts. And his parents were here too. It seemed better for Millie to have a mom — despite the mom that Karen was — and two grandparents nearby, instead of one father who worked 12-hour shifts and had no regular schedule. It was temporary, everything was temporary.

But now — what if his time with Millie had been temporary too?

The doorbell rang, but Leo didn't move. Mom would answer, or Dad, or someone among the large group that congregated here every day. Leo was losing steam.

"Listen, Karen," he said. "I can't be your comfort right now. Go ask one of your boyfriends for help. I just got nothing to give."

She turned on him quickly, from tearful to furious in one second flat. Leo let her vent until she finally hung up.

"Leo?" His mother peered into the room, cracking the door open. "There's someone here to see you."

"Who is it?" Leo set down the remote. All he wanted was some time alone with his little girl.

"It's a lady whose daughter is also missing."

Leo stood. The woman was wringing her hands as she stood at the door. Leo introduced himself. The rest of his family and friends said hello; some came to shake the woman's hand. She didn't look like one of them — and not just because she was white. This woman had certainly never hovered on the poverty line. But her loss brought down all the walls between them.

She said her name was Shantelle. Her daughter had been missing since Katrina.

"Let's go into the kitchen," Leo said.

Mama was already in there making coffee for them both. They sat at the table.

"What do you mean, missing since Katrina?"

"We got separated," Shantelle said, "and she was sent to a shelter. I had to go with my mother — she was dying — I had to go to the hospital. While we were there, someone got my girl."

"Got? How?"

"These people target shelters and places hit by hurricanes and disasters like that. The police were overwhelmed. Later they said she was likely just a runaway, or maybe with some friends. She called once and left a message on my cell phone to say she was all right."

The woman drank her coffee and kept talking. She told Leo more than he ever wished to know. He kept thinking of his own baby, most likely trapped inside the same evil system.

"I'm going back to Louisiana tomorrow," Shantelle finally said. "I heard they're taking a lot of the kids back to service the men working the disaster. Construction crews, cleanup, even aid workers. You can't believe what's been going on in this country of ours."

Leo's head was spinning. He held his temples a moment, squeezing his eyes shut. "To 'service'?"

The woman paused. "Don't you know?"

"What do you mean?" He did know, but he wanted to believe it wasn't true. Wanted to hear her give some miraculous alternative explanation.

"They call it 'pimping them out.' Making them 'hos.'" She gulped hard. "They're making our kids into street whores."

Leo wanted to slam down his hands, grab the table, and toss it across the room. He would kill every man who ever touched his daughter, strangle them until the life left their bulging eyes. If only he could find them. If only he knew where she was. *Hi, Daddy, hi!*

"I'm sorry. I can't hear any more of this." Leo stood up abruptly, grabbing his coat and car keys. He made it as far as the backyard. It was raining. His feet slowed. There was the little swing set his father had helped him build when Millie was three. His legs crumbled beneath him. He clawed the wet ground with his hands, and tears burst from the depths of him.

God, help me. Please help me find her.

***

Rick and Tyler in Vegas

"My wife is going ballistic," Tyler said with a chuckle, rubbing his head. "She thinks I went to a strip club."

The kid's a changed man, Rick thought. Cocky, self-assured.

"And you said you played poker, right?"

"I said I'd call her back, I was in a breakfast meeting with clients."

Rick smiled approval. "Don't admit anything. Start getting mad at her if she won't believe you. Tell her you're out here working, trying to do business for your life there. You went to dinner with the suppliers, then the president invited you to play poker for a few hours. You were doing well — beginner's luck — then you crashed in the room and didn't hear the phone because you put it on vibrate during dinner."

"You're like some *genius* liar!"

Rick shrugged. "It's a talent worth developing."

***

Lacy

Lacy was washing her hair and thinking about everything on her to-do list. She needed to check on the girls, check quotas from the night before, look over the traffic on Bobby's new websites. But her thoughts drifted back to the guy from last night. The sap had given her an extra $300 as a tip for a morning quickie. Lacy decided she'd save it for later in the day — it took care of at least a few tricks. She had never kept money from Bobby. But she was tired. And that 300 bucks would go a long way toward her quota, save her some work tonight.

Tyler would be back to the city for business. He'd call her at least half of those times, she knew. He'd try someone else out probably, but Lacy knew she had gotten the connection. She'd hit the fantasy, not just the experiment. He'd go home with the belief that he'd found his broken angel, a lost soul like him.

Moving her head under the water, Lacy let the soapy water glide over her face. Tyler had been the closest thing to being with a man in love that she could recall. Of course, he wasn't really in love with her. Of course, he was another schmuck paying for sex while a wife slept at home. Of course, all those things — but somehow he had cracked open that old longing again. The longing to be loved by someone. The longing to be saved.

Bobby was the first guy she ever loved. And the first one she ever believed had loved her. But last night, being with Tyler, Lacy wanted to slide into a fantasy as well.

***

Tyler

"What is going on, Tyler?"

Janey's voice on the phone was scratchy with panic. Tyler's delicious afternoon suddenly crashed. Back to his crappy life.

"I lost my phone."

"You said you left your phone in your room."

"I did, I mean, I went back to get it and then I took it down during the business meeting, and then — you know, I don't feel like dealing with this right now."

"You don't feel like dealing with this?" She was getting louder.

"I'm here working to support us. You get to stay home because I'm here doing this. So give me a break, Janey. To get through all the butt-kissing business politics, I had a couple drinks too many, and it didn't sit well, and I was crashed before midnight. My head is killing me."

He was surprised by how convincing he sounded — he felt guilty underneath, but he sounded so good, he nearly believed himself. What was he going to do, confess everything and lose his wife and kid? He'd be another one of those miserable guys with alimony, and child support so high that he couldn't have any hope for a new life. Besides, Tyler didn't want one. He really did love his life. What happened last night had nothing to do with that.

"You have to trust me, baby." He was speaking with a softer tone now. He did feel badly. Janey loved him. She was probably worried sick.

"I'm sorry. Just wish you were home. And you hear so many stories about guys in Vegas on business trips."

"Don't worry. I'll be home tomorrow." And Tyler knew he wouldn't do this again — or at least hardly ever. He wouldn't turn out like Rick, the compulsive liar who reveled in how far he could go without getting caught. Tyler wasn't Rick. He wasn't half the guys at the convention who did this kind of thing all the time. Tyler was a family man. He worked his butt off 50 to 60 hours a week. He was a good dad. He recycled and used green products and put solar in last year. He called his mother once a week; he'd helped pay for his little brother's college. He was a good man. Maybe he wasn't the man he should be right now, not the guy his wife would wish for; but he loved her, he'd do anything for her. The incredible connection he had with the black girl from last night? That had nothing to do with his life in Colorado.

One wild weekend. That was all it was. It meant nothing to his normal life.

It won't affect anything. Everyone has secrets, and when Tyler came here to Vegas, he'd have just one.

***

Rick

"You want a young señorita?" the Mexican guy asked Rick.

It was the same guy he'd used the night before. Probably an illegal working the streets for one of the pimps, handing out cards with phone numbers for girls to everyone who passed by. He was pandering, moving the merchandise, and probably for minimum wage. The real pimp was somewhere else, Rick didn't know where, and it didn't matter. The kind of girl Rick wanted would be protected by that pimp, with this guy as the first contact. But Rick had passed the test. He'd bought and used a girl — proof that he wasn't a cop or FBI. Tonight he'd get what he really wanted.

"You remember me from last night?"

The man grinned. "Yeah, man, I get you a really young one. Barely legal, that what you want?"

"The more 'barely legal' the better, got it, hombre?"

His smile was wide. "Oh, I got it, señor. Barely barely barely legal. She be up in your room one hour."

***

Tyler

Tyler knocked on Rick's room door. He'd been trying to call him all afternoon, but no answer. He heard footsteps coming toward the door, then nothing. Tyler tapped one more time.

The door opened a crack. Rick's face appeared. "Hey, I'm staying in tonight."

"Okay, sure," Tyler replied. "But I think I left my wallet with you."

"Yeah. Hang on."

Tyler heard a crash and peeked his head in. "You okay?"

Then Tyler saw the girl in the bed. His eyes went to Rick — he had knocked over a bottle of rum; it was streaming off the small table and onto the floor. Then he looked at the girl again. *Girl* was the perfect word for her.

Rick swore and grabbed the bottle.

"Hey, here you go." He tossed Tyler his wallet. Tyler missed and had to pick it up off the floor. He couldn't take his eyes off the little girl. She stared at him with enormous brown doe eyes. Her clothes were on the floor. No smile came to her mouth. The sheet was pulled up around her chest. *She wouldn't even have breasts*, Tyler thought, *a girl that age*.

"Problem?" Rick asked in a firm voice.

Tyler opened his mouth, then closed it, shaking his head.

"I'll see you later, then."

Tyler left with a mumbled good-bye. He headed straight for the bar.

Commentary — Who Buys A Child?

I've asked myself again and again.

Who are these men, and sometimes women, who lust after a child?

How can there be each and every year so many men in our country who create the demand for at least 100,000 children in the United States alone ... children being used night after night by men beyond number?

The sheer volume is staggering.

This entire gigantic industry — populated by pimps and facilitators, greased by marketing and millions of dollars — all comes down to one man: the individual man who wants to have sex, or to fantasize about having sex, with a girl or a boy.

What destroyed the moral compass in so many individuals to create such a massive demand? Why is it tolerated in our culture? Where is the feeling of terror, of horror, if there are so many men around us who actually want to have sex with our children?

We should all be asking these questions. And we should be working for change. Because for all of our organization's fighting against it, for all of Shared Hope's work saving and restoring the lives of victims, for all our crafting of new legislation and striving to influence our criminal system — after a decade of continuous, intensive labor — the tragedy goes on. Where something is wanted, for a price, someone will find a way to provide it.

It's time to stop the demand.

Chapter 9

Keep on Trucking

Katie at a truck stop in Texas

Katie pulled down her sweatshirt. She wondered how much longer she could hide her growing belly from Derek and the other girls.

Katie reached up to knock on the door of a semi-truck. "Want some company tonight?"

"Maybe later tonight," came the response — a woman's voice.

"Sure thing. I'll come back 'round." Katie liked the lesbian drivers better than the men. They rarely roughed the girls up, not as much as the guys sometimes did.

Katie walked toward the bathrooms and pulled out a cigarette. Then she noticed the signs: "No Smoking." "No Lot Lizards." She hated that nickname. Some of the other girls found it funny; they even told the truckers their names were Lizzy the Lot Lizard, Gecko-lina, and other ridiculous things. Katie and her stable sisters called themselves Ladies of the Night, not Lot Lizards. They were human beings, after all. She tucked the cigarette behind her ear and headed toward another row of semis lined up for the night.

"What you got?" She heard the door unlock. Katie climbed up the steps and peeked inside to the small cab behind the front seats. Black eyes looked her over. From the light of a small TV screen, Katie could see his face. Hispanic, maybe. Katie knew she might look boring, compared to the girls who got all dolled up with heels and mini-skirts. Katie only wore her jeans and a sweatshirt, but it got her enough business. It seemed to attract fewer of the violent guys. The psychos beat the girls who looked like whores.

He motioned with his head for her to come in. Katie pulled the door behind her and climbed into the small space beside him. He was watching a movie on a small DVD player and drinking something from a mug. He poured liquid from a thermos into another mug and handed it to her. It was soup, and Katie realized how hungry she was. She hadn't eaten all day.

Earlier in the evening, Katie had done a smelly old trucker in an outhouse by the back of the truck stop, and she'd given several blow jobs. Derek had taken all of her money and told her she hadn't earned enough to eat yet. She took a sip of soup — some kind of vegetable with meatballs — and resisted the urge to gulp it down.

"You have baby?" the trucker asked, motioning toward his stomach.

She shook her head.

"Let see," he said.

"No."

"Let me see," he said firmly. Katie pulled up her sweatshirt to reveal the unmistakable five-month bump.

"I have four children. This first?"

Katie nodded, though it wasn't actually her first pregnancy. If Derek found out, this one would be gone like the others. Soon there'd be nothing he could do about it; she'd be too pregnant for an abortion. And finally Katie would have something of her own.

"Do you want me to leave?" she asked him.

"No. It's okay."

"What can I do for you then?"

He considered for a moment, staring at her. "Just, you know, hand, with hand."

"You want a hand job?"

He nodded. "Then you want to watch movie? We could order pizza."

"I'd have to charge for everything if I stay, not just for a hand job."

"Fifty bucks?"

Man, this guy was lonely. "Seventy-five." That was just enough to finish her nightly $500 quota.

He hesitated. He looked her over. "All night then."

The guy seemed decent enough. And Katie had a place to be safe for the night.

"How old are you?"

"Hundred and five," she said. It was her new line that always made the johns laugh. And he did.

Katie left early the next morning while the guy was still snoring. She wished she could go with him. He'd been decent to her, a rare thing indeed. For a moment, she imagined her baby born and the three of them traveling all over the U.S. They could live off soup and pizza. She'd stop smoking and the baby would be healthy, and safe. They'd both be safe.

"What's going to happen to you, my little one?" Katie asked as she rubbed her belly. Somehow she had to make a better life for the kid. She'd do anything to make that happen.

***

A Trucker from Oklahoma

Bill pulled out of the truck stop in Las Vegas, heading along Highway 93 toward Kingman, Arizona. Home in Oklahoma awaited at the end of this long eastbound route.

He chattered with a few people on the radio awhile, then turned on an audio book his daughter had bought him. She was always buying him audio books. Lately, since she'd become all involved in church, she'd been buying him Christian stuff. It mostly bored him to tears, or made him feel guilty for everything he'd ever done. He didn't figure his daughter was actually trying to send him a message that his life was an utter failure and he needed to repent — but still he wondered how to ask her to stop sending the religious ones, and keep on sending the others.

The hours swept by pretty fast. The roads were clear. A crime novel played through the speakers. The time clicked away.

On a stretch of highway through Texas, Bill passed the old truck stop he once stayed at most every week for years. But that was a long time ago. Back then, he'd had a standing appointment with a girl. Bill sometimes thought she had known him better than anyone else on earth. She joked that he was her "mentor." And he couldn't deny that she'd become an expert at her work. They'd met when she was just a kid needing a ride out of the horror of her life. Bill was slow in teaching her what to do and how best to do it. She traveled halfway across the country with him; then Bill called a buddy to take over while he went back home. She traveled like that for months — which Bill knew was safer than the streets. Still, the poor kid met with some pretty rough truckers. He was glad when she finally settled at the truck stop, and he could see her once a week. She liked cherry pie. That was her name: Cherry.

The truck stop was lined up with semis. Bill wondered what had ever happened to Cherry. She wouldn't be a young gal anymore. One week, she was gone from the truck stop. Left word that she'd run to Las Vegas for some reason or another. She didn't work the trucker routes in Vegas, he knew that much; he'd looked for her. Strange how you could miss a whore like that.

Bill decided that tonight, he'd splurge a little. He rarely did it anymore. He thought back to the days when he lived on his CB, when someone would send out a call for a girl and have one as easily as that. Now so many had computers, there wasn't as much action on the CB.

Once, his wife got suspicious, found a lipstick under the cab bench. The threats and tears made him crazy, and the wild streak had run its course in him anyway. These days, when Bill got home, they would barbecue thick steaks and drink beer with their friends. Maybe have his daughter Becky and her softy husband over for dinner so Bill could see his grandson. William's baseball season would be starting. Even with a dad who liked working in an office and being part of church "ministry," as he called it, the kid was a natural athlete. Like his ol' grandpa. It was a good life. He'd worked hard, fought in Nam, and had a flag waving on a pole in the center of his circular driveway. But tonight, he decided, he deserved a rare little treat.

Bill turned around at the next exit. His old truck stop was only a few miles back. He didn't do it hardly ever now. He wasn't like those other guys who hurt the girls. He wasn't hurting anyone. The girl was working, making a living, making a damn good living, even if she had to share it with her pimp.

"Anybody want to talk?"

"What can I get you?" a guy said over the horn.

Bill thought of the old days, of sweet young Cherry.

"Give me something new. As new as you've got."

"Got one for you."

Bill knew the routine. He'd sleep better after.

The knock came within 20 minutes of getting settled. Bill leaned back and opened his pants. The girl smiled, biting her bottom lip. He could tell she loved this — some girls just did.

"You want it?" he asked, glancing down at himself then back to her grin.

"Yes," she said. These girl were like that. They wanted it, loved their jobs, and made the bucks too.

"How old are you?" Bill asked.

"Old enough for you, right?"

She was old enough. She looked young, like an angel, innocent and untouched. And it was a turn-on, no doubt about that. He wouldn't harm a child, but she was no child. Whatever her age really was, she was years older than any 30-year-old he knew.

"What can I do for you?" she asked. In her sweet voice she described each service she offered, and Bill made his selection.

"Careful now, little girl."

He grabbed a fistful of her hair. She was good, better than he remembered it being in a long time. Once he was spent and the rush drifted off, he pushed the girl off his lap. His eye caught a picture of little William in his baseball uniform.

"Here," he said, slightly out of breath and tossing her a 50. "Get lost now."

She pulled up her pants, and he thought of all the men she'd been with. She'd had so many men, and would have so many more. Then he noticed her stomach.

"Are you pregnant?" he asked in disgust.

"No," she said defensively.

There was a knock on his window; a flashlight beam shone in.

"Shit," he said, glancing at the girl. She wasn't as special-looking as he'd first thought. Didn't really look like a whore, more like she could be his grand-kid in her sweatshirt and jeans.

Bill opened the door, ready to make his defense; but the cop shone his light on the lubricant and condom wrapper he'd left on the dashboard.

Bill and the girl hopped down from the truck. Another cop stood a few feet away.

"What are you doing with her?" the officer demanded. Like he didn't already know.

"She stopped by to party a bit. That's all."

"This girl is a minor."

"I asked her if she was legal. She said yes."

That seemed to make the officer pause.

Bill's mind was whirling. He could be fired if he got arrested for solicitation, especially with a minor. He remembered how Charlie lost his job, lost his wife, had to attend some "john school." It really messed up his life. No way did Bill want to go down that road.

"Officer. I'm a hard-working guy, just trying to make a living. It gets a bit lonely out here, and this woman came along and offered a bit of companionship. She didn't tell me she was a minor. I thought we were just having a good time."

"Did you pay her?"

Bill glanced at the other cop, then back to the one talking to him. "No sir, I did not."

"Did he pay you?"

The girl's hesitation was only barely detectable and the officer didn't appear to catch it. "No, he did not."

"Come with us, miss."

"Why?" she asked, and a hand went protectively over her stomach. Bill was repulsed all over again. *She is pregnant.*

"We've received complaints about you going in and out of a number of vehicles this afternoon," the policeman said, "as well as at the portable toilets. The restaurant owner's wife called it in."

The girl swore as one officer handcuffed her and guided her toward the patrol car. The other officer returned Bill's license, registration, and insurance card.

"And sir, don't bullshit me," he said flatly. "Stay away from the hookers before you end up with a disease and taking it home to your wife."

"Sure thing," Bill replied in an apologetic voice. He glanced at the dirty little ho being put into the squad car. It was better they get those girls off the truck stop circuit. They were nothing but trash, luring in good men like himself.

The policemen left, and Bill fired up the truck. He decided to try making it home tonight.

Commentary — Modernized Slavery in the United States

Every kid in the U.S. learns about it over and over before graduating from high school. It begins in kindergarten with drawings of President Lincoln and his dark beard and goes all the way through later years of history class: reading the Emancipation Proclamation, perhaps viewing the movie *Roots*, and studying about our country's citizens divided and fighting one another in the Civil War.

The word *slavery* conjures up horrible images and the reminder of a dark period in U.S. history that continues to influence the country today. Yet despite the struggle over the past, we all believe that slavery was abolished in our nation back in 1864.

We don't think slavery exists today. How could it? We are modern people in one of the most powerful and progressive nations on earth.

On January 1, 1863, Abraham Lincoln issued the Emancipation Proclamation, declaring: "all persons held as slaves within any State or designated part of a State, the people whereof shall then be in rebellion against the United States, shall be then, thenceforward, and forever free."

In January 1865, Congress sent to the state legislatures for ratification what became the Thirteenth Amendment, banning slavery in all U.S. states and territories. The amendment was ratified by December 6, 1865.

Yet, the sad truth is that there are more people enslaved in the world today than ever before in human history.

According to the London-based Anti-Slavery International (ASI), the world's oldest human rights organization, there are at least 27 million people in some form of slavery around the world today. And remarkably, the U.S. contributes enormously to this sad state of the global society.

On October 28, 2000, 135 years after slavery was outlawed by President Abraham Lincoln, the Trafficking Victims Protection Act was passed. It is the first U.S. federal law specifically designed to prevent victimization, protect victims, and prosecute perpetrators of human trafficking. [3] The law also establishes the minimum standards for the elimination of trafficking which the United States Department of State uses to

---

[3]   TVPA 2000, P.L. 106-386. http://frwebgate.access.gpo.gov/cgi-bin/getdoc.cgi?dbname=106_
cong_public_laws&docid=f:publ386.106.

rank countries each year in the Trafficking in Persons (TIP) Report.

Everyone involved in the fight against sex trafficking cheered the Trafficking Victims Protection Act of 2000 (TVPA) as a huge victory and a giant step toward the abolition of human trafficking — modern-day slavery.

What has happened?

A provision in the TVPA requires that the United States Department of State submit a report to the U.S. Congress that details what foreign governments are doing to stop human trafficking. The report is intended to raise global awareness and to "encourage" foreign governments to take effective actions to stop all forms of human trafficking.

One of the first steps in the report is to evaluate whether a country even has a law against trafficking. If they have a law, then the nation is checked to see if it's implementing those laws. Next comes the question of what happens to the victim. Is the trafficked victim arrested or protected and provided safe restorative services?

If a country fails to take significant actions to bring itself into compliance with the minimum standards, it receives a negative assessment. This "bad grade" could mean that the United States will withhold certain non-humanitarian-related aid to that country. The Trafficking in Persons Report details the actions each country has taken to combat trafficking, including passing anti-trafficking legislation, prosecuting traffickers, and providing protection and services to victims. If a country is determined not to take necessary actions, then this is detailed and the country is advised of a timeframe within which such action must be taken.

For example, in 2003, after being ranked on Tier 3 (the worst of three ratings under the Trafficking Victims Protection Act), the Dominican Republic quickly created a new anti-trafficking law to demonstrate its efforts to fight trafficking. Other countries have been criticized for not prosecuting traffickers, or for arresting the victims of trafficking and denying them victim status.

In recent years, the Trafficking in Persons Report has increasingly focused on the situation of children used in commercial sex and labor who are born and enslaved within the borders of the same country — internal trafficking. When I first visited Mumbai, India, and walked through the Falkland Road brothel district, I witnessed internal trafficking. Within

India, children born in India are sold for someone else's profit, then labeled "prostitutes," raped and tortured, and deemed unworthy for justice despite the victimization. There is no safe haven for these children to flee to. And the men buying sex with these children go free.

This atrocious situation in India — which prompted me to found Shared Hope International in 1998 — was appropriately noted in the 2007 Trafficking in Persons Report by the U.S. State Department. "The Ministry of Home Affairs estimates that 90% of India's sex trafficking is internal," it states. The assessment concludes, "India is placed on Tier 2 Watch List for a fourth consecutive year for its failure to show increasing efforts to tackle India's large and multi-dimensional problem." The failures to prosecute traffickers and protect the victims were reported as follows: "Efforts throughout India to investigate and punish trafficking crimes during the past year were uneven and largely inadequate. India's efforts to protect victims of trafficking remain uneven and in many cases inadequate ... unevenly executed across the country because state governments are responsible for implementing the program." The report found that "many victims decline to testify against their traffickers due to the length of proceedings and fear of retribution by traffickers without adequate witness protection from the government." India was assigned to the Tier 2 Watch List as a country whose government was not meeting minimum standards in fighting trafficking and would "be watched" to monitor improvement.

But here's the tragic irony: the very country that reports on foreign governments was not looking within its own borders. Here, in our very midst, was a huge trafficking problem.

The TVPA calls for the evaluation of each country as to the government's efforts in fighting trafficking. One of the first steps in the evaluation is whether the country even has a law against trafficking, and if they have a law, whether the country is implementing those laws. Then, is the victim arrested or protected and provided safe restorative services?

If the State Department assessed its own country, this would be the likely report if evaluated under its own criteria: "In the eight years since the 2000 Trafficking Victims Protection Act was signed into law, the United States has failed to implement an important major provision. While the U.S.

prosecutes those who sell trafficked children, buyers who 'obtain' sex with trafficked children have not been prosecuted and sentenced under this law, a situation that encourages the growing market for sex with younger and younger children. Furthermore, the TVPA states that victims of trafficking cannot be held culpable for the crimes they are compelled to commit while in slavery, yet in nearly every State in the Union, these child victims are arrested and charged with prostitution. Because the U.S. continues to arrest the trafficking victim and does not prosecute the individuals who buy sex from them, they will be placed on the Tier 2 Watch List."

But such a report has not been written by the State Department — because the United States is not included in the TIP Report process. Several reports are written to assess the occurrence of human trafficking and efforts to combat it in the United States pursuant to TVPA requirements in the reauthorizations. Various agencies have individuals or entire units dedicated to fighting human trafficking, especially the human trafficking of foreign victims into the United States. These agencies report on their efforts annually. In the last year, increasing awareness of the scope of domestic sex trafficking has resulted in reports dedicated to the efforts to address it. Nonetheless, none of these reports subject the U.S. to the strict, detailed three-tier ranking system of the Trafficking in Persons Report.

It is time to expose the true scope of trafficking in America — at least 100,000 American children trafficked for sexual exploitation in our cities and towns across America.

It's time for a change.

Chapter 10

Defenders

Officer Tony Riley in Las Vegas

The scent of rotting flesh pervaded the cold morning air as Tony stepped from his squad car. They were on the outskirts of town, at one of the half-finished subdivisions abandoned in the recession. The body was between the garage and the fence of a two-story house. Its windows were smashed out. Graffiti was sprayed over its clean stucco finish.

Tony paused a moment, trying not to inhale the smell. Maxwell was stringing tape and telling onlookers to back off. Tony walked by him, toward the place where Blakes was taking photographs.

The coroner was there too, down on his haunches, talking to Barton. "Dead about two days."

Tony stepped forward. The girl was on her back, legs twisted over in an unnatural pose. One eye had swollen shut, and the other eye stared straight up toward the morning sky. Dirty blonde hair stuck out from a blue wig askew on her head.

"Long-term abuse," the coroner droned, pointing to old bruises and healing scars. "But these bruises" — he pointed to her neck — "are fresh. Looks like strangling. Maybe her neck is broke. I can tell more when we take her in." He was already thinking of her as "Jane Doe" — that's what she would be labeled after being identified as a "working girl." No expensive autopsy or forensics for this one. Not much of an investigation at all.

Two cops Tony didn't know well were talking about the weekend's baseball game — the Diamondbacks had won. This girl would have already been abandoned and rotting by game time. Just like this ghost-town of a subdivision.

All the cops knew this kind of girl; they'd arrested one just like her a hundred times. This wasn't the girl next door; she was just another throwaway. Just another whore.

"This smell is killing me," Blakes said, covering his face with his arm. "We almost done here?"

Tony stared down at the girl and remembered her face. He'd taken her in only a month earlier. She'd screamed and protested like most of them did. Claimed at first her name was Candy, later, admitted it was Leah. Which reminded Tony of his niece. Leah had run away three years earlier. She'd been arrested in Atlanta, but she was gone before any family got there. Eight months, and there still had been no word of her. His brother couldn't recover. He was drinking; his marriage was falling apart. And still Leah was out there.

Tony had an impulse to cover this Leah up, keep her naked corpse from the eyes of the onlookers, from the cops walking around her like she was nothing, worthless. Her breasts had implants and fell at odd angles. Her panties dangled around one ankle. She wore nothing else.

She was just another one. His Leah too. This girl's family might be found if she had one, or if she had someone who cared enough to fill out a missing person's report. But Leah might not be her real name either. Tony thought back and decided he believed her.

"Hey Tony," Maxwell called out, his eyes twinkling with amusement, "she one of yours?"

"Yep," Tony answered sourly, "one of mine." He'd gained a reputation for being a crusader for the prostituted. Suggestions had been made. His wife wasn't happy about it. Tony couldn't blame her; he didn't like it either. He didn't want the speculation. But then here he was again, standing over the body of another child. And ever since Leah, he couldn't keep the faces from coming home with him at night.

"Gotta see things as they are, man," Maxwell was saying. "Some you just can't save. Some aren't even worth saving."

And that was how they all felt. It wasn't just the prevalent attitude. It was standard procedure.

"This one looks used up — at what, 19, maybe?"

He heard laughter and ignored it. As soon as the camera stopped clicking, Tony covered the girl, catching one last glimpse of her face. Her hand stuck from beneath the cover. A bracelet of silver hearts dangled around her wrist. He could picture this girl — Candy or Leah — putting it on, hooking the clasp, admiring it on her wrist. Had she bought it for herself? Or had someone given it to her? *She's just a kid.*

"Here, buddy." Johnson was handing him a cup of coffee. Tony stared down at the girl's hand resting on the cold pavement. "You gotta stop doing this to yourself."

Tony nodded. Johnson understood, though he was smart enough to keep work at work. A few weeks earlier, he had picked Tony up from the bar, and they'd sat together at a diner. Johnson lectured him over pancakes and sausage.

"You can't think too much about it all. It'll make you insane, and I'm not kidding here. Do your job, and then take it off with your uniform — or else get into another line of work. We aren't social workers. We enforce the law and that's it."

Tony knew Johnson was right. His drinking was becoming his only outlet. He had lost his cool a few times at the station, nearly faced suspension. His pastor reminded him that if he left, there'd be one less guy who cared.

But what if this girl was Leah? She was, after all, *somebody's* Leah.

Tony felt the heat of the drink in his hand. Here he was holding a coffee, while this kid was cold and dead. "I should have arrested her over and over again."

"You knew this one?" Johnson asked.

Tony nodded. An airplane swooped down in the distance to land; the rumble of its engines followed behind. "Took her in last month," he said over the noise.

"Jail's about the safest place for these girls."

Tony exhaled. It was true. The law didn't protect them. There weren't enough agencies or volunteers to help. No shelters or foster agencies were prepared for their specific needs. Law enforcement had enough crime to deal with on a daily basis.

At home, Tony had his kid's hockey games, homework to help with, his daughter's training wheels to take off, and a fort that he needed to finish building. He couldn't do it all.

And so — this girl, Leah, was dead. And there was nothing left for him to do except to try not to care. At least not care so much that it screwed up his own life.

He was still figuring out the not caring part.

***

Juvenile Judge Rollins in Las Vegas, Nevada

Judge Robert Rollins pulled into the parking lot of the country club and noted the time on the dash clock. Kathleen and Jane were already eating by the time he found their table.

"We ordered for you," Kathleen said, and took a bite of her salad.

"Thanks," Robert said. His temples were creeping toward another headache. "Anyone got some ibuprofen?" Both women reached for their purses, and he chuckled.

"Hazards of working in law," Jane said with a laugh.

The waiter arrived with Robert's turkey sandwich and Diet Coke.

"So catch me up," Robert said, popping three pills into his mouth.

"I checked on leads for a facility in Henderson. There may be a zoning issue, but the building on Fremont Street is looking pretty good."

Robert had been doubtful that they could get a shelter going in the foreseeable future, but these two women kept surprising him. They not only had a heart for children in prostitution, they had the gumption to get things done.

"Excellent. We need to move on this."

"No kidding. It's like an epidemic," Jane said, shaking her head.

Every Wednesday, Judge Rollins saw the cases for the minors arrested for soliciting sex. They were getting younger, and the number was growing at such a rate that his docket would soon need an extra day.

"Did you hear about the girl this morning?" Kathleen asked, poking at the salad. "She'd been through the system a few months ago."

"Yeah, I had to look her up, but she was one of mine — and yours, Jane."

Robert had first met Jane and Kathleen in the courtroom. Jane stood beside the "child criminals," Kathleen prosecuted them, and Robert judged them. The staggering numbers of prostituted kids got to Jane first; she invited the other two to talk about it over lunch. Robert would never forget her first words: "The system isn't working. And if we don't do something, nothing will ever change on its own."

For six months since that first luncheon, they had met weekly. Progress was slow, a snail's pace. And now another girl was dead.

"I've been studying the work of a Deputy U.S. Attorney in Kansas City," Kathleen said. "She's really going after the johns. She's brought charges against a number of them. I'm compiling the data to present to the D.A.'s office, to maybe get them to do the same here." She leaned back in her chair. "There's a Vegas cop I'd like us to meet with too. Another bleeding heart."

Jane looked doubtful. Robert agreed. Just a week earlier, a girl had been arrested in a sting. The undercover went with the prostitute to her hotel room, instructed the girl to undress completely and then to dance for him. Partway through, five officers broke into the room to arrest her. She was 17. Why did they need six officers to arrest one child prostitute? The cops surely got a kick out of that, retelling it back at the station, getting their rocks off. And this was law enforcement?

"He's different. And they'll lose him if someone doesn't give him some support. We can do that."

"We can't turn this into a support group," Robert said. Their tentative group was now carrying the weight of hundreds of children's lives and futures. Sitting around swapping stories, or arguing over how different law agencies worked, could end up destroying any good they might accomplish.

"No, but this guy, I think this guy could benefit us."

The judge took a bite of his sandwich. Sometimes it struck him how they met weekly in the comfort of the restaurant at an exclusive country club, talking over lunch and Diet Cokes, while hundreds of kids were within their city limit being prostituted at that very moment.

Robert had grown up with a neighbor who survived the Holocaust.

As a young boy hearing the stories of the camps, the death march, the gas chambers, Robert had hated the Germans for not stopping it. They should have stolen guns and saved the people, he'd told his parents. Now here he was dealing with zoning issues to keep kids from being raped and abused. The law, he thought, was the only way to make lasting change.

It just didn't feel like enough.

Commentary — Who Are the Children Trafficked For Sex?

As the sun sets across the United States tonight, thousands of children are rising to meet the night.

They should be in safe homes, in warm beds, being tucked beneath blankets and told bedtime stories.

Instead, they slip into the nocturnal world, dressed for the work of the "track."

All over the United States, these children are being exploited. In Atlanta, Detroit, New York, Kansas City, New Orleans, Seattle, Anchorage, San Francisco, Fort Lauderdale, Denver — in every major city, in the small towns, at truck stops in every State of the Union, they're being put to "work."

People say it's their fault, but I don't think so anymore.

People call them "bad kids," but I don't think so anymore.

People say they like it, some say they *deserve* it. I don't think so.

The Center for Missing and Exploited Children estimates that each year at least 100,000 children are the human products meeting the demand of the sex trafficking industry in the U.S. alone. Around the world, more than one million children are subjected to human trafficking for sex or porn. The industry is estimated to bring in $9.5 billion annually.

The statistics are staggering, but it's the individual stories that are heartbreaking. These are girls as young as 11. Girls who haven't reached puberty. Children who should be in fifth grade. Many have never attended a school dance. Never learned how to use a locker. Never pondered a class schedule.

Their skin is of every color. Some come from "good homes" and have families searching desperately for them. Others are runaways, or children in foster care, who have already been victimized and traumatized within the walls of their homes — and have no one searching for them.

These children had dreams. Some could sing, others danced and put on plays. Some were great at sports or loved to draw and paint. Some girls were shy, in advanced classes, and liked to read at night.

Now they are called *ladies of the night, lot lizards, bitches, whores, sluts, hookers,* and *hos.*

This is America. The land of opportunity. The land of the free, home of the brave. The country of Abraham Lincoln.

Freedom, not slavery, has been abolished for these thousands upon thousands of children ... children who are legal citizens of the greatest nation on earth.

They are America's children. They're our neighbors. They're our children's classmates. They're in our very homes.

They are our children.

We must save them.

Chapter 11

Victims Made Criminal

Star

The trick had been talking for 15 minutes as they sat in the back of his car. He was so friendly that Star didn't have the heart to charge him extra, but they needed to get on with it.

"So do you like what you do?" he asked nervously.

Star smiled. "Of course I do."

"Where's your family?"

She shifted uncomfortably in her seat. Kiki had been giving her advice about dealing with tricks. She'd say for Star to take the bull by the horns, or rather take the man by his....

"Families don't matter too much at the moment, do they?" she replied, arching an eyebrow.

Now he shifted uncomfortably. Star wondered if he had a physical problem.

"Yeah, I guess not. But how old are you?"

She turned even more toward him, moving her thin legs further open. "How old do you want me to be?" Lacy had taught her to say that.

He looked down and smiled. "So do I pay you first?"

"Yes."

He handed her a 50. "Is this enough?"

"Depends on how much time and what all you'd like."

He shrugged. He was sort of cute, in a geeky kind of way. "You do whatever you want."

"Okay." She knew this guy might give her enough to fulfill her quota by the end of this, if she did it right. She tried to remember the videos and instructions, and notice how he responded.

He was easy to please. Star felt a sense of power she hadn't known before. She liked being the one in charge.

Suddenly lights flashed through the back window. The guy jumped and pushed her off his lap. Star grabbed the money and pulled down her skirt.

"I could be your little sister that you're picking up," she told him.

A billy club tapped the window. The john was shaking, not sure what to do. He looked like he might cry. Star wondered if she should run for it. But all the girls had been arrested multiple times. Maybe now it was her turn.

***

Officer Tony

Tony approached the vehicle, then tapped the window. The girl pulled down her short skirt as the man fumbled with his zipper.

"Yes, officer?" the guy said through the closed window.

"I need both of you to exit the vehicle."

The girl was another young one — probably younger than Candy, now resting on a stainless steel table in the morgue. This one was much prettier, still innocent-looking, with full blonde hair and ivory skin. She was surely a hit out here.

Conner pulled up behind him and walked up with a raised eyebrow, no doubt finding it humorous that Tony pulled over a trick — wasting taxpayers' dollars, he'd say. Conner thought the age of consent should change to age 14 — he was vocal about it enough at the station. Tony knew he wouldn't consider 14 okay if it were *his* 14-year-old daughter. They had a fierce argument one day over whether the "little sluts," as Conner liked to call them, "deserved" the life they lived. The argument was going nowhere fast when Tony asked him about his own daughter. Stomping off, Conner shot back that he had raised his daughter with better morals.

"Let the guy go before he craps his pants. We'll haul in the girl."

Within minutes, Tony was leading the cuffed girl toward the car. She tugged against him, looking like she might cry. Usually the girls swore at him, tried spitting in his face, and caused a scene with the other girls on the street.

"What about him?" the girl shrieked, motioning toward the john standing next to his car — shaking, apologizing, begging to be let go. "Why aren't you arresting him?"

Tony ignored her, put her in the back of the squad car, and went back to the guy.

"I should arrest you with her," he told the guy.

"I'm so sorry, sir. I was lonely, and this is the first time I've done this. Please, I have four kids, and my wife would leave me over this."

He deserved to be hauled in, but Tony thought of those four kids and just couldn't do it. It wouldn't really help anything to have a guy like this in jail anyway. Not like the girl — for her, jail was safer than the life out here.

"I don't want to see you down here again. I'll haul your ass in and stick you in with the general population."

"Yes, sir. You won't see me here again. I'm really sorry. Thank you." The man dropped his keys, quickly picked them up, and got back in the car.

The girl was silent now in the back seat. Tony got in the car and paused a moment after calling in to the station.

"I saw one of you dead today."

She stared out the window as if she didn't hear him.

"You want to end up dead?"

She shook her head. "Bobby takes care of me."

"Bobby? Your pimp? Yeah, he'll take care of you all right. It'll be Bobby or some other guy, just like the girl today."

Tony knew the girl would never believe him. He was just another pig to her. She'd be back on the streets. But at least for the next few weeks or months she'd be safe.

He understood. She didn't. And Tony didn't have any idea how to change that.

***

Star

Idiot cops. "Pigs" was the right name for them.

Star thought of every profane name she could as she sat in the cold back seat.

Bobby was going to be furious at her for getting herself arrested. He'd say she should've made the john drive somewhere else. Her quotas would have to be made up when she got out. But Star also knew, when she got through this, she would have proved herself like the other girls. Cherry had been arrested the most — she couldn't even remember how many times she'd caught a case. Kiki and Brandi were tied at eight. Lacy was smarter and had only been picked up four times. Loyalty could only be demonstrated by action. And here she was proving her loyalty. Star would never tell them about Bobby — even if they tried the good cop/bad cop routine, or threatened her with prison.

"Sweeping more scum off the street," the other cop growled, then walked back toward his car.

The cop tried to talk to her. Star wanted to spit in his face. It was exactly like Bobby and the girls said — the cops arrested her and treated her like a piece of trash.

As the cop drove, Star thought she saw Brandi — on her corner, a few blocks away, leaning into a car.

"Funny how only the hos get arrested," Star said. "It takes two to party."

The stupid pig didn't answer. He tried saying something about Candy, like he cared. Everyone was talking about it, and everyone knew it was Blade who done it. Candy was dead because she was stupid. She tried trading up to Bobby at the exact wrong time. Blade wasn't very forgiving.

Bobby cared for Star and her wife-in-laws. Bobby might yell at her, but he'd hold her close when the others weren't there. She was his baby girl. He'd be mad for a while, but after this he'd take her to get something pretty at the mall. A new outfit and her nails done. She might have to share him, but he did take care of her like he promised. Bobby kept his promises, the good ones and the bad. But he kept them. Nobody was looking for her, nobody cared.

No one but Bobby.

***

Doris in Lincoln, Nebraska

Doris stirred her tea with a tiny spoon that shook in her hand. The spoon said *Seattle* on the handle; the shape of the Space Needle was cut into the metal. Cassie had loved their spoon collection. Doris had started it years before her granddaughter's birth. Together they'd gone through her old collection, and added new pieces whenever they traveled.

The house was silent except for the sound of the refrigerator and the lonesome cry of a train far-off. Doris carried her teacup toward the living room, but she stopped at the piano instead of the couch.

She sat at the bench and touched a key, remembering her little granddaughter's feet dangling far above the carpeted floor as she practiced the scales and *Mary Had a Little Lamb*.

On top of the piano was a standing parade of framed photographs. Beth holding Cassie as an infant. Beth, Ryan, and Cassie a few months before the fatal crash that took Ryan and sent Beth down the road toward destruction. Each of Cassie's school pictures from first to sixth grade.

She wondered if there would be any more school pictures in the future.

"My girl, my little girl," Doris called into the night. "Where are you?"

The world was so big now, especially with the cancer stealing her energy. Everything was harder for her, tiring. Even a cup of tea, even another night of prayers and tears. And little Cassie knew nothing about it.

Resting her head in her hands, her elbows crunched down into the piano keys, Doris tried to hold back the tears. All the faces were gone now. Walter, Beth, Ryan, and now Cassie. And Doris would leave too.

"Our Father, who art in heaven, hallowed be thy Name...." Doris couldn't go further.

Sure, she checked in regularly with the Center for Missing and Exploited Children, but there had been no word. She had seen the flyer about her granddaughter on a bulletin board at WalMart. It had stopped her in her tracks. She left her shopping cart in the middle of the entrance and fled in horror.

Doris straightened and inhaled sharply and tapped the piano keys. She could almost feel Cassie's presence beside her, still a little girl. Doris had taught her piano; she had taught her the Lord's Prayer and the 23rd Psalm. She had the songs and the prayer ... yet her little granddaughter was lost somewhere in the great big world.

Mary ... had ... a ... little ... lamb. Yea, though I walk through the valley of the shadow of death ... little lamb, little lamb ... I will fear no evil, for Thou art with me.

***

Star in Juvenile Jail

Star couldn't sleep. The cell was cold. The other girls in the room moaned or cried or stomped around as if they were the only ones there. Fear pulsed through her; she wanted to scream and scream until they let her out. It was all she could do to keep from falling apart — like the girl who started banging her head against the wall until blood dripped down her hair and the guards took her away.

It was the longest night of her life.

Star must have eventually slept because morning was suddenly there, with everyone up and heading to chow. She ate some disgusting slop — something they tried to pass off as egg casserole — then she was called to talk with the public defender. She knew Bobby couldn't come see her in juvy, but she longed to see him. She imagined them putting their hands up to the glass, if there were glass, and he'd promise to be waiting when she got out.

There was no glass divider when Star was set down with Jane — her public defender. Star might have liked Jane if not for the circumstances. But Jane's legal assistant Mr. Thomas looked like her Uncle Frank — Uncle Frank, who was actually the neighbor, not an uncle at all. He had fixed her bicycle chain once. He was always nice, pushing up his glasses and talking. But then there was that night, the Fourth of July, when Uncle Frank smelled like beer and sweat. He asked Star to help him get his ice chest out of the garage.

"You're such a beautiful girl," Uncle Frank said that night — many times — and many times more, and in the nights to come.

Mr. Thomas was going through Star's file while Jane explained the process of going before the judge.

Star couldn't stop fidgeting. If there were any chance of escaping, she intended to go for it.

"You lived with your grandmother in Lincoln?" Mr. Thomas asked. Star wanted to ask if he could leave. Plus, she hated answering questions when Mr. Thomas already had the answer right in front of him.

"Yeah," she answered, staring at her hands.

"How old are you?"

"Eighteen."

"Eighteen?" He gave her a long look that said, *Do you think we're that stupid?*

"Uh-huh." Star gave him a hard stare until he looked back at the file.

"According to the info with Missing and Exploited Children," he replied, "you're 13 now."

Star shrugged, but it surprised her to think of her face on one of those milk cartons, or in the ads at a supermarket. Had Grandma Doris done that?

Jane folded her hands. "Cassie, your pimp doesn't really care about you. He's just using you to get money."

Star wanted to slap this woman. *Who does she think she is, anyway?* She was wearing her nice suit and carrying her leather briefcase. What did she know about the street, or how people had to love each other out in the real world? Star wouldn't trade lives with this lady for a million dollars. Well, maybe for a million.

"I have a boyfriend who takes care of me," Star answered firmly.

"And what do you have to do for your boyfriend? Does he make you work? Does he make you have sex with men? Does he beat you? Do you see any of the money?"

Star shook her head vehemently. "Nobody makes me do anything. I decide what I do and what I don't do."

"You're 13 years old. You're too young to decide these things. Someone helps you decide them, and you don't even realize it."

"I do what I want. Nobody makes me do anything." This stupid woman didn't know the first thing about her life. And why would Star ever tell her?

Commentary — What's Happening in Our Legal System?

In February 2009, one of our team members was in Florida training police officers on how to identify and work with prostituted children out on the street.

Other police stations had responded wonderfully to the training videos, which show victims' perspectives and feature our undercover investigations.

But at this training, one older officer interrupted the session. "Why do we need all of this?" he demanded. "If they'd just lower the age of consent, then we wouldn't have this problem."

Our trainer paused a moment, a bit shocked by his blatant attitude — even though she knew from experience that this was a prevailing school of thought. None of the other officers spoke up, either to agree or disagree with him.

"So a child at that age should have the right to have sex with a man who is your age?" our trainer asked. "What if that 14-year-old was your daughter? Would you still want the age of consent to be 14?"

The officer didn't back down a bit. "My daughter wouldn't do it," he insisted. "She has morals. I taught my daughter better than that."

When I heard it, this statement left me shaking my head. To this man, his daughter and her friends would be of more worth because of *where they came from.*

But it's not an uncommon thought.

And yet, where would half of us be if our value were established by such criteria?

Where would our world be?

These girls have the value of priceless treasure. They should be protected by our law enforcement, treated and helped as *the victims that they are.*

There are great police officers and law enforcement agencies all over our nation. Many are frustrated by the system. Some arrest these children because there's no other way to protect the girls than to put them in jail. The officers and the lawyers know the girls won't get help. They know the girls won't reform or go back to their families, if they have families to return to.

They know this child is getting a police record that will follow her the rest of her life.

But at least a girl is alive for another day.

I've seen, in recent years, a gradual shift — a welcome shift — in the system's treatment of child victims. "Prostitutes" who are actually children are finally being seen as child victims instead of child criminals. And this change in *labeling* is monumentally important. It's helped us restore more girls' lives.

Juvenile hall and jail are not the answer. A victim should not be incarcerated and be saddled with a criminal record.

Changing the law so that a 14-year-old has the "right of consent" is not the answer. What child can understand how vast an effect such a "decision" will have upon her life?

We want these children to be alive. But we want much more. They need to be rescued, restored — and they need laws, law enforcement policies, that will *stop the trade*.

Chapter 12

Law Without Justice

Star in Las Vegas Juvenile Court

Wearing an orange jumpsuit, Star walked into the courtroom — and immediately spotted her grandmother. Doris rose from her bench and covered her mouth with a trembling hand.

"Oh, sweetie!" she cried out, bursting into tears.

Star's mind reeled. Seeing Grandma Doris was like a flashback in a movie. Life in Nebraska seemed so far away. A place she could never return to. A dream she'd once had, but couldn't entirely remember.

And there was Judge Rollins. Star had heard all about him from the other girls who'd been through this scene again and again. He acted hard-nosed and scary, but he cared. "Pretend like you're really sorry. Say that you want to rehabilitate. Plead guilty, it'll go faster. Cry if you can."

Star thought of Bobby non-stop. Did he miss her? Was he worried? Would he be proud of her for this? The other girls had all been arrested; it was just one of the downsides to the life. Star hated being in juvenile detention with kids who had murdered people, stolen cars, raped other kids, set baby kittens on fire, who knew what else — but she kept reminding herself that *now she too* had completely proven her loyalty to Bobby.

Star didn't really listen to the judge or her public defender. They were trying to get her "help." She didn't need help; she just needed to be allowed to live her own life. Emancipated — what did that mean? Tried as an adult — huh?

"You'll be released," the judge finally said, "into the care of your grandmother."

"No," Star replied. "I don't want to go with her."

The judge gave her a long stare. "It's either that or you remain in juvenile detention for the next three months."

Star shook her head. "I want to live on my own." She could hear Grandma Doris sniffling behind her. It was driving her crazy.

"How are you going to do that?"

"I'll get a job."

"You are 13 years old. It's not legal for an employer to hire you."

Star chuckled. She'd already had plenty of employers in the four months since she'd come to Las Vegas.

The judge was chewing her out for being a ho. *Blah, blah, blah*, she kept saying in her head. What did he know? He sat behind a giant desk and was probably out picking up girls after work.

And then just like that, it was over. She was "remanded into the care" of her grandmother. Star turned toward her grandma. *What next?* she wondered. She let Grandma Doris hold her and cry. But the old woman's touch felt cold and distant to her.

"I've been so worried," Doris gasped. "Just so very worried."

Star didn't have anything to say. The free lawyer lady had paperwork for them to sign; there was a long discussion. Star tried ignoring it all. When it was time to change clothes, Star figured she'd put her street clothes back on — clothes that stank of sweat and cigarette smoke. But Grandma Doris had brought her clothing from "home." The shirt had once been a favorite of hers, bright pink with white hearts. She felt like a silly little girl wearing it over her baggy jeans — jeans that proved how much weight she had lost in the past four months, just like she'd hoped!

Grandma Doris had driven to Vegas with her friend — instead of flying, since she didn't know how long it would take before Star was released. The friend had left, a week ago. Now, as they drove back to Nebraska, Star would have to put up with two full days of listening to her grandmother's emotional diary of the past four months.

In the first half hour, they didn't speak much. Star felt herself getting panicky as every mile took her further from Bobby. What was he doing right at that moment? Was he going crazy worrying about her? What were the other girls doing? Did they know she was free — but headed back to Nebraska?

"I've prayed so many times," Grandma Doris was blubbering, "and I was so afraid. So very, very afraid."

"I'm fine," Star said again. "I'm sorry you were worried. I should have told you I was okay."

She couldn't deny the guilt. She could just imagine her grandmother weeping day and night in her little house. But now, the idea of going back there — back to the scent of old people, back to the doilies on the tables, the politeness and correctness of everything — she'd want to kill herself.

"I can't believe what you've become," Grandma said, shaking her head and crying. "If your mother could see you."

Star's cheeks stung, as if her grandmother had slapped her. Grandma Doris was sobbing now, clutching the steering wheel. What could Star say? Yes, she was a ho. Yes, she was pimped out. Yes, she'd had sex with more guys than Grandma could imagine. Grandma had been with one man her entire life. She'd always taught Star to be chaste — who even *used* such a word anymore? *Stay a virgin till you're married*, she'd told Star. Grandma didn't know that "Uncle" Frank made that impossible — from the time Star was 10 years old.

"I don't mean to judge, sweetie," Grandma Doris whined. "We'll get some help for you. For me too. It's not easy being raised by an old lady. But I'm so glad that you're back."

Star pictured Mindy. Her old best friend. Did Mindy have sex with that boyfriend she was keeping a secret from her mom? Maybe. But whether she had or not, what would Star say when Mindy asked — and she *knew* she would ask: *How many men have you had sex with? How many have you given blow jobs to?*

How could Star give a number? There had to be more than a hundred. Maybe four hundred, in the four months she'd been with Bobby. Sex was nothing to her now. Before, it was something they'd whisper about. Mindy would be like that still. Mindy wouldn't know how to make a man climax. She wouldn't know the keys to survival — what if a john turned mean? What if more than one turned up at the party? Her friends at home would be horrified by what she'd seen, what she'd done, what had been done to her.

And what about the kids at her school? The boys she had liked, her other friends. They'd all find out what she'd done ... that she'd been in jail. They probably already knew.

She could not go back.

Suddenly Star couldn't breathe; she took a sharp gasp of air and felt the tension in her chest. The old life was tugging at her, tearing her into two.

I cannot go back there.

And what about Bobby? *He loves me. I would do anything for him.*

"I have to go to the bathroom, Grandma."

"Okay, sweetie, I saw there's a rest stop ahead. At the next town, maybe we can find a Dairy Queen and get a little treat. I know you haven't had many treats lately."

Grandma, you have no idea the treats I've had.

Grandma Doris was talking about church, how the pastor's wife was going to meet with her. Star heard her voice from far away. She'd bought new curtains for Star's room. Guilt! But Star swallowed it. She just couldn't go back.

Her grandmother parked, unhooked her seat belt. Star had already opened her door and hopped out. She thought about stealing Grandma Doris' purse, but no. She could make it without hurting her even more.

"Listen, Grandma. I love you. Don't worry about me, okay? I can take care of myself now. I'll call you. I'll come visit."

The old woman's face was a puzzle of wrinkles. "What do you mean?"

Star leaned in from the street. "I can't come with you. I just can't."

Grandma's eyes flashed. "I'll — I'll call the police." She was stuttering. "They said you have to stay with me. You have to check in with them."

Star looked around at the landscape, then put her face back in the car window. "It's okay, Grandma. I have people who take care of me. I have a boyfriend."

Doris set her jaw. "You mean a pimp?"

"He's not my pimp. He's helping me to go places. Please, Grandma, don't worry. I'll call you soon."

"Wait — Cassie — please!"

She tried to get out, but she stopped. Star had already taken a step away.

"Wait!" the old woman croaked.

Star's face was flushed. Doris could see her teeth as she spat out the words. "I'll see you in a few months. I'll come visit. I promise."

Star pushed off from the side of the car and ran across the parking lot. A row of semi-trucks — she waved to one just starting to pull out. It slowed. The driver rolled down his window.

"Heading back to Vegas?" she called.

"Yeah," he answered, his lower lip stuck out by a huge wad of chew. His beard and hair looked like he'd been living in the woods for a month.

Star glanced back to see if Grandma Doris was in sight. No. Good.

"Can I get a ride?"

The trucker hesitated.

"We could trade?" Star offered brightly.

Now it was his turn to glance around.

He opened his door.

"Sure, get in."

Commentary — When I Grow Up

When I grow up, I want to be a prostitute.

I want to be used by men however they wish.

And I'll say, "Oh baby, yes, I love it, I love everything about you." And I'll hold back my vomit and keep on my smiles to convince them, so they'll stop slapping me. But because I love it, because I love the taste of everything about them, they'll say I'm a slut, a dirty little girl who needs to be punished. They'll burn cigarettes into my skin, jab me anyplace they like, bloody my nose, blacken my eyes, laugh at my tears, hold a gun to my head, cut me, tattoo me, as their eyes grow large and excited. I'll scream and cry and beg because I can't act anymore.

I don't want to be riding a pink bicycle with a basket in the front. I hate the little girls with their hands held tight by fathers, fathers who look at me in disgust and cover their daughters' eyes so they don't see me. I don't want to be one of those girls with a decorated bedroom and frilly pillows on my bed. I don't want to giggle and talk about whether a boy likes me or not. I don't want to decide for myself whether to wait for marriage to have sex and remain a virgin.

When I grow up, I don't want to attend college, consider joining a sorority, or have my own apartment. I don't want to try different career paths or figure out who I am. I don't wish for a wedding day in a church or on a beach with bridesmaids, a dad walking me down the aisle, little flower petals beneath my feet. Who cares about baby showers or decorating a nursery? I don't want to learn how to cook or decide between being a stay-at-home mom or a working mother. I don't want any of those things.

Because when I grow up, I want to be a prostitute.

Can anyone believe that?

Chapter 13

Business as Usual

Star in Las Vegas

"Hookers Day at the mall!" Brandi laughed.

The five women were walking together — and passed another group of women dressed in what Cherry called "ho-wear."

They'd been shopping all afternoon for new outfits. Star, lugging her bags, wondered what Bobby would think of her new bra and panties. In the weeks since she'd been back from the brink of Nebraska, she'd hoped for more of Bobby — more attention, more time, more anything. But he was overwhelmed, preparing for fight night. At least he had slipped her an extra 40, and told her not to tell the other girls. That was something.

Lacy had explained it to Star. Bobby splurged like this once or twice a year on them. They all got their nails done, bodies waxed, new heels, underwear, bras, perfume. Star knew Bobby would treat her like that all the time, except that he had to be fair to the others. It wouldn't always be that way, he kept promising. She was the only one he was taking to the photo shoots, he reminded her.

Back at the apartment, Bobby was smoking a bong in front of the TV with two other guys.

"I hope you bought some nice things for once," he snarled. "We'll have some high-classed clients, so try not to look like the skanks you are."

All the guys laughed, Bobby included.

Bobby's stressing, Lacy had told Star. Sure, Lacy was bottom ho. She believed Bobby needed her, to run things smoothly. But Star knew the truth. The truth about *Bobby and Star*. Lacy didn't know what Bobby told her. Lacy, Bobby had told Star confidentially, wasn't nearly as important as she thought.

Star sat next to him. "What did you buy?" Bobby asked. He grabbed the edge of the Victoria's Secret bag. She smiled at him — he always loved her smile, she could tell. It was just that his attention was distracted by Brandi — who happened to be squealing over a little dog in a TV commercial. Ever since Brandi's third abortion, all she could talk about was getting a little dog.

"We don't need no dog around here," Bobby said — which launched Brandi on an emotional tirade. The men started yelling at her for blocking the TV.

Star tugged on Bobby's shirt. "Let's go in the other room."

"Brandi!" Bobby yelled. "Get the hell out of the way!"

Star leaned toward him. "I'll show you my new—"

The pain didn't register for a moment. She was stunned by the elbow driving into her nose.

"Will — you — get — *off* me a minute?!"

"Bobby!" Cherry yelled from the kitchen. "You gave her a bloody nose!"

It took another moment for Star to realize Cherry was talking about her. Blood was pouring all over her clothes, into the bag on her lap.

"Shut up, Cherry! Brandi! Get the hell out of here!" Bobby shrieked. "I worked nonstop the past week! I want one afternoon off! Can't you bitches leave me alone?"

Cherry rushed a dishtowel in from the kitchen. Star pushed it to her face.

Bobby grabbed the Victoria's Secret bag.

"Look at this!" He threw it at her. "You've got blood all inside this bag, I'm not paying for more. You better find a way to clean it."

He began screaming threats and profanity. The girls cowered. Star — her head back, the towel to her nose — realized she was sobbing.

Bobby was heading toward the door.

"I'm out of here. A man can't even relax in his own house."

***

Lacy

From her bed upstairs, Lacy heard the commotion.

The rest of the girls loved shopping, but it just wore her out. She liked her new clothes, new nails, and all that. But she'd been ready to come home hours earlier. She wanted to sleep before they worked tonight.

They were in a townhouse now, for the past few weeks. "Putting down roots," Bobby called it. Lacy knew it was more than that. They always moved around. It was a fact of life. It was required. But for a few months, some stability was needed. A townhouse; that would be good. Bobby had a lot of irons in the fire. Too many, Lacy thought. He was building his online cybersex and porn sites — going more virtual, and making a killing at it. He had his girls — who needed constant managing. In the past, he'd had as many as 15 girls in his stable. Now his five weren't bringing in the money he would've liked. But they were a good core; they met the diverse needs of his clients. In a week was the fight. Bobby was maxed out — beyond maxed out with all of it.

It was quiet again downstairs, and Lacy was nearly asleep, when she heard a shout from downstairs.

"Lacy! Get down here, Lacy!"

It was Bobby. She knew he might blame her for something one of the other girls did. The downside of being Bobby's right hand was the responsibility — and the punishment — she took when something went wrong. Which was often. She had decided that one work hazard of a bottom ho was to have at least one or more bruises to hide with make-up.

Bobby stood at the downstairs doorway. Lacy flew down the stairs. There was Star, crying, with a rag held to her nose, looking at Lacy as if *Lacy* were the guilty party. This kid needed to get a clue about the way things worked around here. The other girls got it, knew their places.

Bobby got on the phone and headed toward the parking lot. Lacy had to hurry to catch up. He was swearing violently. "I don't give a shit about some story of a father in Kansas City," he raged. "What do you take me for? This is business. You get me the product and I pay you. Don't give me your lame-assed excuses. You said you'd deliver and I expect it to happen. Send 'em or bring 'em, I don't care how they get here, just get 'em. I've got more orders than I can fill, and that's not even touching the ones coming in."

Lacy leaned against the metal fence railing with her eyes out toward the flashing lights of the city. She looked at a billboard advertising a singer, one her older sister had liked when they were kids.

Bobby swore again as he hung up and moved toward the car. She didn't say a word till they were sitting inside with the engine purring. The engine always soothed something in Bobby. Maybe 'cause his daddy had a car like this, and he'd take Bobby around New Jersey, checking on his whores, teaching his boy the life.

But now Bobby kept shaking his head.

"What's the deal?" Lacy finally asked.

"Everybody's all jumpy ever since the raid. Ricco don't want to drive the girls himself, so he's sending 'em. Now we got these girls from Kansas City coming in by Greyhound. *Greyhound.* You gotta pick 'em up. I'm not taking chances some hot-to-trot vice takes our property a day before fight night."

"Sure, baby. No problem."

Lacy took a breath. "What's up with the thing about some father?"

"Just what we need. Ricco got this new girl. Had her a week or something. Guess her pop is all over the media, got his church out passing around fliers. Holding prayer vigils. Even though the cops got her up as a runaway. Ricco don't want to bring the girl back to Missouri after the fight. We'll probably keep her. Idiot. This is why I hate working out-of-state."

"It'll be fine, baby. We'll get the girls for fight night, and it's all good to bring a new girl into the stable. We've had more than six before. I'll groom her."

Bobby's eyes stayed closed. He breathed out. Lacy knew everything would be just fine.

She wondered how Star would respond to a new girl in the stable. It made her smile just thinking about it. That little whore wasn't going to like it at all.

***

Lacy at Greyhound in Las Vegas, Nevada

Summer was coming on, but this evening held on to the cool spring.

Lacy wore jeans and a T-shirt, trying to blend in with the other civilians getting their bus passes or picking up travelers at the Greyhound station. It felt strange to look "normal" for a little while. She felt a little invisible; she wasn't sure if that was a good thing or not. Maybe she liked the attention, being a woman of the night, more than she realized.

From the screen over the ticket counter, Lacy read that the bus was just coming in. She followed the signs to the unloading area. Workers opened the belly of the bus and pulled out the luggage. A few minutes later the passengers started departing. Bobby was expecting 15 girls from Kansas City. Ricco was sending girls in groups, some now and some tomorrow. Then Bobby had 10 more coming in from Atlanta. They were gonna be hopping.

Lacy knew she'd be managing a handful. That was all right with her.

She almost chuckled watching the girls getting off the bus. If Bobby was looking to have them blend in, he needed to have a little chat with these hos. There was no mistaking their profession — not with their gawdy, tight outfits, furry coats, and boots. She counted six girls; one was still missing. Lacy laughed to herself, thinking she should have held up a sign: "Hos from Kansas City."

"I'm your ride," Lacy said, approaching the girls who flocked together. They looked at her with suspicion. "Kansas City, right? Here to see Bobby Bad?"

They looked relieved. *Hookers from anywhere*, she said to herself — *they all look the same*. Skanky older white woman, reminded her of Cherry or Belle. Three Hispanics hanging together, pencil lines for eyebrows. Two other white girls.

"Where's the other one?"

Lacy stopped cold. A young black girl stepped down the stairs, a backpack slung over her shoulder.

"Girl," the older woman said, "get over here." The other girls came closer. There were a few looks from other departing passengers.

"Welcome to Vegas," Lacy announced like a tour guide; "glad you made it. I parked out here."

The girls got their luggage and followed her out. There was plenty of complaining about the trip. "We're starving" — lots of that stuff.

Lacy glanced back, again and again, at the black girl. *It can't be*, she thought. *There is absolutely no way.*

"Come here," she finally said to the girl.

The girl came quickly. She seemed relieved to be away from the white woman in charge.

"Where you from?" Lacy asked her.

"Kansas City, Missouri."

Lacy kept looking at the kid as they walked through the station. "Yeah, I figured. But before that."

"I always been there."

Lacy frowned. It was uncanny how much this girl looked like her little sister. "You in the system?"

"System?"

"Foster care? Or do you have a mom and dad?"

"I have a mom and her boyfriends. My daddy too, but he's been working out of town a long time."

"Ah." This was the girl with the daddy who was making trouble. There was no way this girl was Mishka — though Lacy's little sister would be about this age. Lacy hadn't seen Mishka for five years. This girl looked like she could be her sister's twin.

"How old are you?"

"Eleven."

This girl looked even younger than 11. It sent an ache through Lacy's chest. *Star looks old compared to this kid.* Lacy put her arm around the girl, but the girl flinched and pulled away.

"What's your name?"

The girl glanced up at Lacy. "Sugar."

"Sugar, huh?" Lacy wanted to know her real name, but she knew it wasn't good to remind the kid of home right now. She had a very busy week ahead.

And somehow it made Lacy cringe, every time she looked at the girl.

"Okay, I've got a van for us," Lacy called to the girls. "This way." She turned to Sugar. "I'll carry your backpack." She was surprised by its light weight. Lacy reached her hand out, and the girl took it — her hand was soft and small. A wave of emotion washed through Lacy. It was like nothing she'd felt since — well, maybe like nothing she'd ever known at all.

Commentary — Why Don't They Leave?

So why don't they leave?

We can only understand by stepping into their shoes.

We have to see into their world, their reality, their norm.

While *any* child is vulnerable to being targeted and recruited by a pimp, the reality is that pimps seek out youth who are experiencing strife in the family, such as verbal, physical, or sexual abuse. According to the FBI, one in four females and one in eight males will be sexually abused before the age of 18 — a disturbing statistic which means that the pond for pimps to fish in is quite large.

I encourage you for a moment to really try to place yourself in the shoes of this child. A child whose understanding of the world is constructed in a chronically abusive environment where secrecy and exploitation are the forced norm. A child survivor of sex trafficking once told me, "My child sexual abuse is where I learned the rules of prostitution — life was always about exchanging favors for favors." "When people ask me why I didn't report the incest," another survivor said, "I wonder why no one ever told *me* it was abuse."

And now I turn to you and challenge you to consider why we are asking *why she didn't run away* when we ought to be asking, *Who are these sick men targeting and preying upon our children to buy and sell them?* Let's put the focus, let's place the blame, on the perpetrator, the kidnapper, the child rapist, the torturer — not the victim!

In the words of Mickey Royal, a self-proclaimed pimp who wrote the 1998 book *The Pimp Game: Instruction Guide*:

> A ho's desire can't be fed because she has a need that isn't
> material — security, love, acceptance, confirmation of
> one's sense of self worth, etc. Just as young men join gangs
> for the same reason, a ho exchanges something she can
> see for something she can't. This leaves the door open for
> exploitation, abuse, and misuse.

Then the pimp begins to engage in a game of establishing trust — something Royal calls "an intricate process of psychological destruction and emotional construction": his every move is designed to identify the needs, hopes, and dreams of the child so he can meet the needs and exploit the hopes and dreams. Meanwhile, the pimp is taking care of basic needs such as food, clothing, and shelter to establish a level of physical and psychological dependency.

The result: a hostage situation. The child's every move, the child's every thought, is built around whether it would please the pimp. The youth is emotionally, physically, psychologically, and financially dependent on the pimp. This orchestrated hostage environment sets the stage for the youth to develop "trauma bonds" — or the "Stockholm Syndrome," where a victim shows signs of loyalty and love to an abuser. The level of attachment is often impacted by the length of time that the abuser and victim have available to bond. In the case of child sex trafficking, it's often months to years.

Mickey Royal is by no means the only pimp proud of his established methods of exploitation, documenting and touting his success. R.J. Martin has written a paper actually showing how to use the famous "Maslow's Hierarchy of Needs" to "make the most money." The article provides details on how to use each stage of the hierarchy for the manipulation and control of a child or woman. Pimps call it "The Pyramid"; it systematically addresses foundational human needs such as safety/security, love, and belonging — and shows how past sexual abuse, family dysfunction, societal judgment, and systemic failure leave gaps for pimps to fill. By offering a false sense of security, respect, and love, Martin points out, a pimp can establish a traumatic bond that will keep the girl on the street every night and large amounts of cash flowing into his hands.

The final tactic that a pimp uses to secure the loyalty and love of his child victim is to keep the original dream of a "real life together" alive by assuring the victim that the prostitution is only temporary. After a long night of servicing 20 to 30 strangers, then returning "home" and handing all the money over, the pimp will reinforce "the dreams they have together," whatever they may be. Royal puts it this way:

> A pimp sells a ho a dream like a manager promises to take
> her to Hollywood and make her a star. By the time she
> realizes she's been had, she's trapped. A ho is in pursuit
> of her own fantasy and she feels that the pimp knows

the directions or is already there. She can't leave because tomorrow **might** be that day. That day when the dream or fantasy she's chasing comes true. The same reason why that horse can't stop pulling the plow. The horse believes that each step, each pull of the plow brings a new hope of the dream coming true, eating the carrot.

These girls live in a world where they have no feminists reminding them of their rights. She has no man who does more than make promises about helping her, before he uses her for his own lust. And the systems they've come into contact with — Child Protective Services and Juvenile Justice — have failed to save them. These girls have come to believe they only have worth and value as sexual beings. They are trapped in a prison of this subculture, only streets away from where all of us live.

Understanding why they don't leave "the life," we can find greater compassion for these women and children, and see them truly as victims.

When I meet them, they often act anything but the victim. They can be tough, crude, suspicious, angry, hate-filled, neurotic, violent — and/or living a fantasy. But all of this is *what has kept them alive.*

Why else don't they run away?

- The fear of physical abuse inflicted by a pimp if she is caught.
- The girls are brainwashed into "loving" their pimp and believing despite what he does to her that her pimp loves her in return.
- They are taught to distrust law enforcement and social service providers. This distrust is proven when they are arrested and charged as criminals in the U.S. courts.
- They have no money of their own.
- They feel shame for what they've become outside of the "street" society.
- They find acceptance in their subculture.

I encourage you to ask not why they didn't run away, but what horrible things must have happened to these children — to keep them quiet in a world where every day and night is a living nightmare!

Every little girl — no matter if she's 10 or 25, 30 or 50 — is worth saving.

Chapter 14

When Love Sneaks In

Lacy

Lacy woke drenched in sweat. She wondered if she'd called out in her sleep. But the room was silent — except for the gentle sound of breathing, and the more distant snoring. The snoring would be Cherry, in the next room.

The dream had been vivid. All the events were muddled up. Belle was in it. Her sisters. Bobby too. Lacy tried to sort through it, but found the memory fading fast. Something about her life before she met Bobby.

The clock said 11:00 a.m. A thin stream of light danced in the curtains. They all usually slept until early afternoon or later. But Lacy knew she wouldn't be sleeping any longer. She sat on the edge of the bed naked and chilled as the sweat cooled on her body. Bobby was already gone — or maybe he was in someone else's bed.

Bobby. The dream had been about meeting him. That was a time she had tried to forget. Wondering what life might have been was worthless. It only made her angry at him — which had backfired on her every time.

He'd been so charming. Lacy instinctively smiled, just thinking about it. She'd never felt anything like that before — a cool older guy being interested in her. Her, and her alone. She remembered the first time she saw him. She was walking home from school. Strangely, Lacy remembered that she was working out an idea for a story she had to write for Advanced English, the group her seventh grade teacher had put her in. A story about an old house, by the sea, with broken-out windows.

Bobby had leaned out his window, pulling up beside her in a dark low rider. The bass from the stereo thumped low and steady. "Hey, come here, girl."

Lacy had kept walking, glancing over and trying not to smile as he followed. She knew she should be scared, but he wasn't no serial killer. He was cute, really cute, and much older. He kept pace with her, even when a car honked behind him and went around.

"Come over here a second. I ain't gonna hurt you. I won't even get out of my car. I just need directions."

Lacy looked around. There was an outdoor bistro up the street and a few cars going by. She was safe enough. So she walked over.

He quickly became her boyfriend. She couldn't believe it. At first Lacy didn't tell a soul. Bobby said it was better that way; people wouldn't understand. Every day, week after week, he caught up with her going to and from school. He brought little gifts — and on Valentine's Day, a heart-shaped box of candy.

They fell in love fast. Bobby wanted her all to himself. Her friends complained that she didn't do anything with them anymore. Lacy's older sister threatened to tell Mama.

When she was with Bobby, the world disappeared. He taught her about music, they went to the arcade and he won her a giant bear, he gave her a first taste of alcohol and crack. And he went slow about having sex with her. There was no pressure like her mom said guys would do. Bobby wanted her, he was nearly out of his mind wanting her — it was a thrill to have someone desire her like that. He showed her how much, asked her to touch him, then he used her hand and showed her what he liked. But he didn't touch her until she wanted it. And the more they were together, the more she wanted him — until the night they finally made love.

After that, Lacy was all his. She knew she'd be with him for the rest of her life. He started getting busy with his work, but still he made time to see her every day.

"What do you do for work?" she asked, realizing she knew very little about him outside of what they had together.

"I'm a pimp, don't you know, baby?"

Lacy laughed at that. "Are you?"

"I am. You don't believe me? Someday you'll believe me." Then they'd make love, slow and tender ... then rougher as the time went. She carried the secret with her. Her friends and older sister acted like silly children. They gossiped about who had smoked pot or got drunk for the first time. They were shocked when they learned that someone they knew had sex. Lacy didn't want to be around them. And Bobby wanted her with him, so she didn't mind missing the first school dance. That stuff was for kids.

Months passed like that. Lacy got grounded for sneaking out of the house. She snuck out anyway.

"Baby, we need some money," Bobby said one day. "I don't know what we're gonna do." Lacy was sitting on the couch in his friend's apartment. Bobby was upset, like nothing she'd seen before. "I owe this guy money. I may have to leave the state if I can't find a way to pay him. But I just can't stand the thought of being away from you."

"You can't leave. Maybe I could get a job or something."

"Oh girl, I love you. I really love you, you know that, right?"

Lacy beamed. She did know it.

"I can't believe I have to ask this of you." He looked like he might cry. He took a hit and Lacy knew the surge he was feeling as he did. He passed it to her. Bobby made her limit it: not every day, only on special occasions. He was always taking care of her.

"I'd do anything for you," Lacy said, and she would. She felt the rush flow through her body. She'd die for him. Anything.

"Listen, Jason likes you...."

And the rest just swirled together. All the things Bobby said, all the months after that. Until Lacy had left one life behind her, and started a new one with Bobby Bad.

You have to do this.
Don't you want us to be together?
I hate it too.
I can't be here, it'll drive me mad.
Thank you for doing that.
I never had anyone love me like you do.
Baby, there's this guy ... it's just a blow job.
You aren't cheating on me, I know what we have.
We're just doing this for a while, then we'll have the money to start a life together.

Those are my other girls.
They work for me, but they don't have nothing like we have.
We're moving off the West Coast.
I can't go without you.
Won't it be great in Vegas....

Lacy had done anything and everything for him. She thought he'd do anything for her too. He loved her, and someday they'd have a house and a regular life. They'd have babies then, and a white picket fence, the whole package. That was what they were working for.

Then one day, Lacy walked in and saw him in bed with two of the other girls. One was on top of him. Lacy screamed and pulled the girl off by her hair. Bobby started laughing.

Lacy knew then. She was a ho. He was her pimp. One of his other girls had said it; now the lights were on. The journey from star student, Advanced English, to *hooker selling herself on the streets* was a hazy memory, a trail she couldn't quite recall.

Lacy was packing up her clothes when Bobby had found her.

"Where you going?" Bobby had asked, blocking the door.

"Away from here!"

"Where you going? You got nowhere to go."

"I'm going home."

"With what money? You gonna screw your way somewhere? You gonna renegade out there alone? How long until you're dead in some ditch?"

"I'll call my mom, she'll come get me."

"Your mom doesn't want a whore in her house," Bobby replied coolly. "You'll disgust her, and she won't want you to *infect your sisters*. Look at you. You look like a whore, you act like one, you get paid to be one, and you certainly smell like one." Bobby snorted. Lacy stopped packing.

"Where's your money? You *owe* me money," Bobby sneered, "for all the taking care of you that I do. Baby, you aren't going anywhere."

She pushed toward the door, but he began to beat her. Then he shoved her into a closet. She cried and screamed, finally she begged. She was locked in there for hours. No water, no food, no escape to the bathroom. None of her pleas were answered. It felt like days. She grew weak and then weaker, until she was so thirsty, she tried clawing her way through the door.

She thought she was dead — but it was Bobby gathering her up in his arms. He carefully gave her water. And then she felt his tears.

"Baby, why do you do this to me? You know I love you. You know this is what I gotta do. It won't be like this forever. I can't give you all the attention, them other girls will get jealous and leave us. We gotta manage 'em. We can do it together."

Now, years later, Lacy sat on the edge of the bed and remembered it all. She thought of the little girl Sugar, asleep on the couch downstairs. It had been five years since Lacy met Bobby. She was 17 now, turning 18 soon. The little girl was only 11.

***

Lacy and Sugar

Fight night kept them all in chaos. Bobby was stressed; he'd be beating every girl within reach if he wasn't too concerned about them looking good. He had tickets for the fight; he was already gone, with Star and Kiki at his elbows. They'd be working the party Bobby was attending afterward.

Lacy had to manage 20 girls while still working herself. She had schedules. She had a *spreadsheet*. She'd figured out how to make it on the computer. It listed which girls were needed where and at what times. Some were going to parties after the fight; one girl was attending the fight; a few had solo gigs; some would be gone for the weekend. In the middle of the insanity, Lacy took 10 minutes in the bathroom at a hotel to prep Sugar, to see if the kid was ready — and make sure she wasn't catching too much grief from Star. Lacy had reveled in the white girl's jealousy over little black Sugar. But she also knew it could be a problem — once fight weekend was over and Sugar stayed in the stable.

Lacy pulled the flat iron through the girl's kinky hair. Her bronze skin was soft. Her cheeks still had some baby roundness.

"This your first big event, right?" Lacy asked. She was wondering what Sugar would encounter tonight.

The girl nodded.

"Did your dad abuse you?"

Sugar looked surprised at the question. Lacy couldn't blame her. It was an odd thing for her to ask, especially right now.

"No."

"He never touched you?"

Sugar looked disgusted by that. "No way. My daddy was a deacon at the church. He teached Sunday school, before he had to work out of town."

"Well, why didn't you say so? If I had a dime for every churchy guy...." But then Lacy decided to drop it. "So, do you miss your daddy?"

Sugar clenched her jaw and looked away.

"Why'd you run away then? Why are you here?"

Still the girl didn't look in her direction.

"Look at me now." Lacy turned the girl's chin to face her.

"Why did you run away?"

She shook her head. Tears pooled in her dark eyes. Her dark honey skin was smooth, silky — perfect.

"My mom let me do whatever I wanted. When Daddy was back in town, he was too strict. Never let me do anything with my friends. Mom wasn't taking care of me, so he was talking about getting custody and moving me to Milwaukee. Then my mom's boyfriend...."

Sugar looked down.

"I can guess," Lacy said.

"He never touched me. But he kept looking at me like he might. I just wanted to get away. So I thought I'd visit my aunt in Florida. But when I went down to the bus station, they wouldn't let me buy a ticket."

She stopped. Lacy was surprised at all she'd poured out.

"Then you met someone who said he'd take care of you."

Sugar nodded. Her black eyes were so wide, so deep.

"Now I can't ever go back."

Lacy didn't have to ask why. It was the same reason none of them went back. If girls like them had homes to return to, someone — anyone who would open the door — they wouldn't want to tell the stories of where they'd been. How could they integrate back into normal life? But most of the girls had no place to go, no one to call, no one to care, no one who even knew they existed.

"My daddy," Sugar said quietly, "would never want me back now."

Lacy knew she should be going over their list of rules again. This kid would need quick seasoning, a sudden plunge into the life. But Lacy's mouth couldn't take her there. And when her phone showed the location of Sugar's first trick, Lacy knew exactly who it was and how he liked it. Sugar wasn't a virgin — Lacy knew that by the way the kid had come in, wincing as she sat down — but not even Bobby had had his turn with her yet. Sugar hadn't been turned quite yet.

"Listen. I'll take care of your dates tonight."

Lacy was surprised by her own words. Yet the decision was made. She could make both their quotas, and Bobby would be none the wiser. And though the fight would keep Lacy busy, it could also help hide Sugar. He'd beat both of them if he found out, might even kill them. He'd call it a betrayal. She couldn't let him know.

"What about your dates?"

"I can do them both, it's not that hard for me. You stay here in the hotel and hide out. Don't leave or do anything, okay?"

Sugar nodded.

Lacy bit her lip as she looked around the room. "I'm taking both of the keys to the room. If someone knocks on the door, don't answer. You aren't here. Promise me, don't answer."

"Okay." Sugar seemed to understand.

"You can watch TV if you turn it real low. I'll be back before morning, maybe sooner to check on you."

"Come check on me, please."

The tremor in Sugar's voice, the touch of vulnerability, wrenched Lacy's heart. And it strengthened her resolve to do this.

"I'll try, but I'll be busy. If I can't come, you just wait here until I get back. I'm taking your phone with me. Just wait here."

Sugar nodded again.

"I promise."

***

Katie in Texas

Her belly was growing. Now the baby was kicking regularly, and often had the hiccups.

Katie hated the women's home she'd been sent to by the judge. Soon, she'd be transferred to a place somewhere else — she figured she would hate that too. But at least her baby was safe. No one could force her to have an abortion, and Katie could decide whether to keep her baby or give the infant to a family.

All around her, people were encouraging her to give the baby up. Katie had quit smoking, hadn't had one in two weeks. She dreamed of a life with her child, even if she was only a child herself. But Katie also knew who she was. And what kind of life could a kid have with a mom who was a ho?

***

Lacy

Lacy couldn't sleep again. Bobby was still out, and most of the girls were in bed. Sugar was asleep in Lacy's bed beside her; Star and Kiki were in the other queen bed across from them.

She sat up, smoking and flipping through infomercials on the TV. Once in a while she glanced down at Sugar, a picture of perfect peace, her hands folded under her cheek.

Lacy's body ached from the night. But she felt a rush of power, too, along with the pain. Looking at the little girl, Lacy had a feeling of protectiveness that she'd never known with anyone. The idea of someone hurting this girl sent rage through her veins — Lacy could kill someone, she realized.

She barely touched the girl's wiry black hair. "She can't stay here," she whispered aloud.

"What did you say?" Star said from the other bed. She was awake and staring at her, the light of the television flashing on her face.

"Nothing." Lacy took a drag from her cigarette and stared at the screen. A couple walked through their mansion and showed off their luxury cars.

"What's wrong?" Star asked, sitting up more.

"Nothing. But hey, you did well tonight."

Star smiled. "Bobby said I made the most, out of all the girls."

Bobby, Bobby, Bobby. It was always the same with Star.

"I never saw Sugar out there," Star said. Her tone told Lacy she knew what Lacy had done.

"Of course you didn't. You were partying all night and raking in a killing." Lacy would deny it to the end, and Bobby wouldn't believe Star over her.

"Yeah, I didn't see you much either."

"Training you girls is a big job. Don't forget who taught you."

Star smiled and nodded. "I love you, Lacy. Don't worry."

Don't worry about what? Was that a threat?

"What do I have to worry over?"

Star shrugged, but it was clear to Lacy, the kid had big ideas swirling around in her head. Star figured she could be Bobby's bottom ho, Bobby's main girl. It was hilarious. Who did she think she was? Five months earlier, she was sobbing in an empty bathtub; now she was acting all high and mighty.

Star then — and Star now. With those twin images came the memory of herself then — and herself now. She was Jessica back in those days — plain old Jessica. Now, for five years — ever since she was 12 years old — she'd been Lacy.

And that decided it.

Lacy wouldn't let the same thing happen to Sugar.

This kid might actually have a shot at life.

Lacy was done believing she had any future of her own. There were no big dreams to come true. No house and kids. No white picket fence. No high class anything. Lacy might end up a high class ho, but that was the best she could hope for. Even that was fading, every day she got older.

"Go to sleep, Star. We need it after this weekend."

Lacy put out her cigarette and slid back down into the blankets. She could feel the rhythmic breathing of the little girl beside her.

She'd find a way to save Sugar. No matter the cost.

***

Lacy winced with every step she walked. She'd awakened sore after fight night, then had to go to a party; and again she had taken Sugar's tricks. At least now the fight was over. She had to heal. Those adrenaline-infused johns, all riled up from seeing men smashing other men's faces — they always took it out on the girls.

"Owie, owie, owie," she whispered to herself, walking up to the house. It might be time to visit the free clinic. But later. Tonight, Lacy needed to get high on something. Bobby wouldn't let them smoke crack or shoot up on work nights, but now that it was over, Lacy could use something. He'd certainly have them back on the normal routine by nightfall.

But as she walked into the townhouse, she stopped cold. Sugar was sitting on the couch, tears streaming down her face.

"What is it? What happened?' Lacy hurried inside, looking daggers in every direction.

"We didn't do anything to her," Star said with annoyance, carrying a plate to the couch. "I made pancakes, though."

Lacy was surprised to find the other girls there. Lacy had sent Sugar home to an empty house a few hours earlier. But now Brandi, Cherry, and Kiki were all eating at the table. The other girls were at hotels, or heading back to their various cities as the fight weekend wound down.

Sugar pulled out earbuds. The kid was listening to her iPod.

"What are you listening to?" She opened her purse and looked for the bottle of pills.

"I just love that Taylor Swift song about Romeo and Juliet."

"Oh, yeah!" the others chimed in. "Me too."

Lacy sighed heavily and shook her head.

"You've heard it," Sugar insisted, "everyone's heard it." She put the headphones up to Lacy's ears and pushed a button. A sweet melody filled

Lacy's ears for a moment or two, then she jerked away.

"See? That one."

"Yeah, I guess I've heard it around," Lacy muttered.

"Were Romeo and Juliet real people?"

Lacy took two long white pills and popped them into her mouth. She followed it with a swig of vodka. She willed the drugs and alcohol to quench the fire between her legs. She had another party in an hour, which would mean a long night of pain. Still, with the pain came a certain satisfaction: that Sugar wasn't feeling any of it.

"It's one of Shakespeare's plays — you've heard of him, right?"

Sugar twisted her mouth. "Maybe."

"He's some famous dead writer. From England, I think, or — yeah, England." She thought of the movie *Shakespeare in Love*. "One of Shakespeare's plays was Romeo and Juliet. I don't think they were real people, just characters in his story."

"Oh." Sugar frowned.

"I never seen the play, but I saw the movie about Romeo and Juliet with Leonardo DiCaprio. It's modern, but it follows the same story as the old one, the England one." Sugar wasn't following her, Lacy could tell. "Romeo and Juliet were these teenagers whose families hated each other. They're sworn enemies. But at a masquerade ball, Romeo and Juliet meet, and that night they fall in love."

"In one night?"

Sugar stretched out on the couch, like a little kid ready to hear a bedtime story.

"Yep," Cherry chimed in from the table, her mouth full of pancakes. "It was a love-at-first-sight kind of thing."

"Doesn't anyone else know the story?" Lacy asked. The needles of pain were getting to her.

Kiki laughed. "I only know that part that's something about 'Romeo, Romeo, wherefore art thou Romeo.'"

Lacy winced as she sat on the couch beside Sugar. The kid pulled up her thin legs. Lacy felt something like pride welling up in her over this little girl. Sugar hadn't opened her legs for one man throughout the entire fight weekend. Lacy didn't want her ever to open them again, not until she was married.

From the way the others were acting, either their little ruse had worked, or the other girls didn't care that Lacy was protecting Sugar.

"Lacy, you tell the rest of it," Cherry said.

"I don't tell stories all that well. I just know they sneaked around, but then a few people die, and the feud gets worse, or something like that. At the end, they were both dead."

"Who was?" Sugar asked with shock on her face.

Star dropped her fork. "Romeo and Juliet? They die?"

The other girls at the table howled.

"Children today," Kiki squealed, "they don't know nothin' about the classics!"

Cherry spoke with mock concern. "What are our children being taught?"

But the expressions on Sugar and Star's faces sobered the laughter.

"Is that what happened?" Sugar demanded.

"Juliet and the priest came up with a plan," Lacy said, "to make it look like she had died. She drank a poison that would make her look dead. But Romeo didn't get the message. He thought she really was dead. So when he saw her in her coffin, he killed himself. Then Juliet awoke and found Romeo dead, so she killed herself too. "

Brandi spoke from the table. "They loved each other so much, they didn't want to live without each other."

Cherry sighed heavily. "I wish someone would love me that much."

The room fell silent.

"There was this trucker a long time ago," Cherry finally said. "I thought he might love me, but ... well, you know. He weren't no Romeo."

Lacy thought of Bobby. Bobby certainly didn't love her enough to die for her. Not one man she'd ever known would have given up his life to save hers.

Kiki jumped up. "Let's listen to the song." She took Sugar's iPod and stuck it in Bobby's stereo — something none of them was allowed to touch.

The music began. Lacy felt the ache in her body cutting through her heart. She wanted to hold Sugar close — or run for the door. She felt hot tears on her face. There they sat, a house full of whores, listening to a song about true love. White dresses. Marriage. Forever.

Then they turned down the lights and all sat on the floor by the couch to listen to the song a second time. Lacy took a line of crank. She told Sugar to leave it alone, but she handed her the vodka bottle. Everyone needed something at a time like this.

There would be no flowing white dress, no man on his knee, no forever. Not for Lacy. That kind of dream had killed more than one girl she knew. It would destroy her too. Lacy was made for men like Bobby Bad, not a man like Romeo. Not someone who would love her to such lengths, such depths, that he'd die without her.

But it can happen for my little Sugar.

Lacy would give her that chance.

***

Lacy and Sugar in Las Vegas

Lacy burst into the hotel room.

"We've got to leave."

She had rented the room for Sugar to hide in every night that week.

"Why?" Sugar hopped up from the bed. The TV was on.

"Bobby wants you at his party tonight. I said I'd bring you in an hour."

Sugar nodded. She knew what that meant.

"We'll stop by the townhouse on our way out."

They took a cab. Lacy considered leaving Sugar there while she ran in for some of their things, but she wanted to keep the girl close. Stopping at the townhouse could be a mistake; she knew they could get caught there. But she decided they needed at least a few decent clothes for getting out of Vegas and heading east.

"Wish we could dye our hair, like in the movies," Sugar said as they packed up their few belongings.

Lacy laughed at the idea — two black girls dying their hair to try hiding from Bobby.

"Wish we could dye our *skin* for a few days, that's what I wish."

Lacy checked the closet to make sure she hadn't missed anything. The girls were all working — like the two of them were supposed to be. Lacy wanted to be able to tell them good-bye — especially Cherry. She slid a note into the older woman's drawer, asking her to tell the rest of them good-bye. For Bobby, she had no words — just a middle finger in the air.

"Hurry up now. We need to be out of here in five minutes."

Bobby would be partying it up with his pals — he shouldn't be stopping by the townhouse for anything — but Lacy didn't want to take any chances.

Sugar zipped her backpack. "I don't have any money."

"I made a little this afternoon. I'll work when we need money."

Sugar bit her lip. Lacy hurried into the bathroom for her toiletries. They'd had to act normal the last two days, knowing they were leaving, but not knowing when. It was that text — ordering Sugar for Bobby's party — that told Lacy it was time to go.

Lacy tossed her make-up in her bag, then turned to look at Sugar. The little girl had her backpack on her back, ready to go.

"Hey, what's your name? Your real name?"

Sugar's big black eyes danced.

"Millie! Millie Taylor."

"Millie, I'm Jessica, but you can still call me Lacy if you want. I've been Lacy a very long time."

"I want to call you Jessica."

Lacy breathed in. She hadn't been called Jessica in five years, and it might take a while getting used to; but it felt good.

"Where are we going?" Millie asked.

"Kansas City."

Millie shook her head. "No. I don't want to see my dad."

"He loves you. You've gotta put all of this behind you."

Lacy's phone rang — it was Bobby's ringtone. He always sent her a text. Now he was calling?

"We gotta get outta here — now."

***

Bobby and Star

Bobby slammed down his phone.

"What did I tell you?" Star sneered.

Lacy hadn't answered him, and she *always* answered him.

"Turn down the music!" Bobby yelled. He walked out the door of the hotel room. Star followed fast on his heels. Bobby was texting furiously into his phone, pacing up and down the street.

"Why didn't you tell me any of this before?"

Star cringed. "I didn't know for sure. I just suspected she was protecting her."

"It makes sense," Bobby snarled, "it makes perfect sense. I was too busy to notice. No one said they'd actually been with Sugar. I didn't get no word back on her. I just can't believe Lacy would do this."

"Lacy said she reminded her of her little sister."

Bobby's phone buzzed with a text message. He read it aloud: "We're on our way, baby. You're still at the party, right?"

He typed back, with Star leaning close to see what he wrote. *Where you at?*

There was no reply.

"I'm going to the house," Bobby said. "And they better be there."

***

FBI Agent Jimmy Lopez — Las Vegas, Nevada

Agent Lopez was missing his son's school play. Lance was playing an important supporting role. But Jimmy would have to watch it on video — as he had so many other of his young son's accomplishments.

He didn't like working vice. He didn't like being in Vegas. But this guy Tony seemed okay. They sat in a small office in the FBI's Vegas headquarters building, leaning over a desk covered in photographs. The connection with Bobby Bad — that's how Jimmy had been pulled into the raid. Here was a mid-level Vegas pimp with ties to both West and Midwest circuits. Prostitution, drugs, possibly guns, possibly more.

"We missed picking him up during the fight weekend," Tony was explaining. "I wanted to move, but then your guys came in."

Jimmy nodded. "Yeah, that would've been a good time; but like it or not, working together is the best move for this one. We want this guy to turn state's evidence."

"So this guy will walk?" Tony said, irritation in his voice. He picked up a surveillance photo of Bobby.

"Probably not walk. We'll have to see what he gives us. But we won't make a deal with his crony." He tossed another photo. "Right here — Blade? That's his name?"

"Yeah, Blade."

Tony picked up a photo of the dead girl, Leah. "We need to get him for something, since we can't get him for this."

"These raids are progress, I suppose."

Officer Tony took a drink of his coffee. Jimmy had never tasted a worse cup of brew — but Tony didn't seem to mind it.

"I can't wait to see the looks on their faces. Bobby Bad thinks he's got Vegas in the palm of his hand. He has no idea. His party days are about to end. And you know? I may go visit Blade in prison after he's some guy's bitch, to see how he likes it."

Jimmy snorted. "I'll drive you there myself."

***

Star and Bobby

Bobby swung his hand across the table. Glasses and fingernail polish went flying; a lamp exploded on the floor.

"I'll kill her!" he yelled. He stalked to the closet, reached up to a shelf, and pulled down a box. There was a gun in it.

"Bobby, please. It'll be okay. We don't need her. We can make it without her."

"You stupid or something?" Bobby's eyes were blazing. "You have no idea how much time and money I just lost. I got a client paying top price for Sugar tonight. Lacy's the only one who knows what to do for half my clients. When I find her — and I will find her — she's going to wish she never met me."

"I can take Sugar's client," Star pleaded. "Please, Bobby, let me take him tonight. Let me try. "

This was her chance. If she could prove herself to Bobby — make herself invaluable — prove that they didn't need Lacy — he might make her bottom ho. Even though she was young.

Bobby paused. Star imagined him being jealous, unsure whether he wanted to give her up to the client. But she'd show him how important she was, invaluable to him.

"I want to do it."

He looked at his watch and nodded. "I'll send you a text where to go." He was walking out. "I've got a lot to figure out tonight."

He slammed the door. *He's mad at Lacy*, Star told herself. *If he wasn't so angry at Lacy, he would've kissed me good-bye. He woulda seen what I'm doing for him. He will soon enough.*

***

Star somewhere in the Nevada foothills

Star had never seen such an ugly man in her life. Grandma Doris would have scolded her for thinking something mean like that, but it was true. He was an old guy — at least 50 — and really fat. His nose looked like a clown nose — red and wide and bumpy. His face had deep crevices and marks.

"You're late!" he barked as she hopped into his car in the Circus

Circus parking lot. His eyes were as dark as his tone. His wide mouth reminded her of a giant fish her grandpa had brought home from the lake when she was small. A bass, she remembered.

"I'll make it up to you," Star said with a smile.

"You better believe you'll make it up to me. I paid your guy a lot of money. And how old are you?"

"Are you a cop?"

He laughed. "No, honey, I'm not a cop. How old are you?"

"Eleven," she lied. Bobby's instructions. The client specifically requested an 11-year-old.

He glared at her. "You look older than that. What year were you born?"

Star shrugged. "I don't know. I just know my birthday is next month, and I'll turn 12."

He grunted. "Let's go for a drive."

"Sure thing, baby."

But Star felt a nauseous wave of fear. She clutched the phone. She wondered if she should call Bobby. No. He'd say she couldn't handle it, just like he figured. And her shot at bottom ho would be lost.

They drove off the main streets and onto the highway. The man didn't speak. They drove further than Star expected. Finally, he exited the highway. Then more driving — and eventually they stopped at a house. He made a call on his cell phone. Another guy came out of the house and hopped in the back seat. He said nothing — just reached over the seat and grabbed her purse.

"Hey, give me that back."

The driver smacked her hard in the face. Her nose spurted blood — she flashed back to the day Bobby had elbowed her. Both men laughed. Star looked around for something to hold against her nose. She wished they'd slow down again — she'd dive out of the car. She could make it up to Bobby somehow. But then Star heard the doors lock.

"Where's your cell phone?" the guy in the back seat asked. He was well-dressed and smelled of expensive cologne.

Star handed it over, filled with dread. They drove a long time. It felt like an hour before they pulled down a long driveway to a secluded cabin. Star hadn't been this far outside of the city. It would have been pretty — if not for the eerie darkness.

"Welcome home," the guy in the back seat chuckled. The ugly man stopped the car and turned to face her.

"We're not taking you back."

"What do you mean?" she asked, trembling.

"He paid your pimp well, but not good enough for all the stuff we're going to do to you."

He turned off the engine. Star clutched the seat with her hands.

"Come inside," the driver said.

She could hear the other man laughing.

***

The body of a young woman was found three months later in the foothills above Las Vegas.

The sun had beat down hard on the barren land and the corpse.

Dental records were matched to a runaway on the database of the Center for Missing and Exploited Children.

An elderly woman, the girl's only remaining relative, received the call.

The girl had been stabbed multiple times.

She was two months pregnant.

The body was shipped to her hometown in Nebraska, where she was buried beside her mother; the girl's grandmother had bought the plot for herself.

A few people from the church attended the short graveside service. The photograph on the memorial program was a school picture from sixth grade. It was the last photo of the girl her grandmother had.

Chapter 15

Hope for America's Children

Jessica and Millie (formerly Lacy and Sugar) in Kansas City

Jessica was starting to really like the place.

She'd figured when they got to Kansas City, she'd take Millie straight to her house — or to the police. Then Jessica was going to head south to Florida, where she could find a new pimp — a more powerful one, who could save her from Bobby if he ever found her.

But plans changed.

Millie insisted Jessica remain with her when they went to meet her father. It was a teary reunion. There was no question this dad would take his little one back. Jessica tried to slink away, but Millie's father asked her to stay. He arranged for her to stay awhile with a woman from the church. Then he worked with local law enforcement to find her a place at a women's shelter.

Jessica wasn't allowed to talk to Millie much now. She missed the little girl terribly, but she could understand the restriction. The cops thought it best for the kid. Millie's dad said he wanted to adopt Jessica, but Jessica wouldn't hear of it. She didn't want some "family life." Not yet, anyway. The idea of it creeped her out.

The women's shelter? It was okay. They gave her a journal. Sometimes she wrote in it. She was taking classes too, learning to cook! She remembered baking brownies and tiny little cakes in her Easy Bake Oven when she was a girl — but that was the extent of her baking experience. Still, she was really liking it. She seemed to have a knack for the kitchen. It made her happy when people complimented something she made.

It wasn't paradise, of course. Jessica couldn't stand some of the other girls. Some didn't have a clue what real life was like out there on the street. One woman, a shelter volunteer, was even a virgin — that floored Jessica. Once when Jessica was joking about men and their erections, the girl turned a color that she didn't know white people could turn. That's when the girl said — with a bit of pride, Jessica thought — that she'd never been with a man. Like it was some great accomplishment or something. But then, yeah, a secret part of Jessica wished she were a virgin. But then she snickered at herself. *I wish I could fly too. Or become a mermaid!*

She did have one friend. Katie understood the life. She'd lived for two years at a truck stop in Texas. Now the girl was pregnant — barely 15 years old. Jessica didn't know if they'd let Katie keep her baby or what would happen — but then none of them really knew what would happen.

A lot of the time, Jessica still felt like "Lacy." She was glad Millie went to counseling, glad she was being home-schooled until next year, after which the kid would probably go back to school. Jessica figured it would be good if no one knew her past; otherwise the knowing could destroy her. Guys would come around, offering, and girls would hate her.

Bobby was in jail, awaiting his federal trial, but Jessica still kept a wary eye out. She worried about Millie too. Bobby might send someone out for them. Jessica warned Millie's dad by email — more than once. But with every passing month, they all felt better.

***

Jessica sat at the computer. She was doing some work for the shelter, entering names, helping make fliers. Today, during her break, she went to Facebook and did a search.

That's where she found her.

Mishka Houston.

Her little sister shouldn't have a Facebook page — that was Jessica's first thought. The profile was set to "private," but the photo was public — and a beautiful girl was smiling for the camera. Jessica leaned in close, inspecting her clothing, trying to detect anything in her eyes. Everything looked normal. A regular girl, about to start high school.

Jessica was feeling ready to start reaching out to her sisters. She'd start with Michelle, the eldest; she was attending community college in Fresno.

And then maybe, just maybe, Jessica could salvage a little of her life ... and help other girls like her. That's what she wanted now.

It felt pretty good to want something like this. Could something good could come from her life after all? Maybe it could.

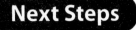

Next Steps

(conclusions from National Report on DMST)

Next Step #1: U.S. citizens and lawful permanent resident child victims of sex trafficking must not be criminalized.

There is a dichotomy between the treatment of domestically trafficked minors and their status as victims. Despite being recognized as victims by the majority of participants in all ten assessment sites, these victims are being labeled and treated as delinquents. This criminalization creates barriers to service delivery and infringes on victim rights to which domestic minor sex trafficking victims should have access. The solution requires harmonization of laws to ensure minors exploited through commercial sexual acts are not charged with a crime. Also, proper safe placements are required such that law enforcement, prosecutors, and the judiciary are not compelled to criminalize a domestic minor sex trafficking victim for the purpose of securing her for her own safety and/or for continued access to her as a witness.

Next Step #2: The arrest and prosecution of buyers must be made a priority.

Buyers are not arrested and prosecuted as frequently as necessary to deter the crime of solicitation. Though tremendous efforts have been taken to combat traffickers and other sexual exploiters, buyers have not been targeted. Demand is the root cause of domestic minor sex trafficking. Buyers of sex acts with children must face substantial penalties and coordinated efforts to hold them accountable. Recent indictments of buyers under the federal TVPA is a promising development, as buyers will face the severe penalties of the TVPA, increasing the deterrent effect of the federal law.

Next Step #3: Domestic minor sex trafficking must be recognized as a national threat.

Domestic minor sex trafficking is a burgeoning criminal enterprise in America. Gangs are turning to prostituting minors as a less risky source of revenue than drug trafficking or other crimes. Traffickers of foreign victims into the U.S. are finding local, American children easier to recruit and sell without the difficulties of crossing borders. Communities are being adversely affected with the loss of hundreds of thousands of children to this victimization. Resources must be committed and a zero-tolerance standard must be implemented at the law enforcement level with regard to buyers of sex from minors to attack the trafficker networks as well as the buyers presenting the demand in this market.

Next Step #4: Innovative investigative techniques, technology, and protocols are needed to combat domestic minor sex trafficking.

Traffickers, facilitators, and buyers use innovative methods to market, sell, and buy children, therefore, investigations must be equally innovative. Current methods must be assessed and law enforcement entities that have been addressing domestic minor sex trafficking can provide evidence-based techniques. Investigative protocols for the treatment of the victims were notably absent in several of the assessment sites, but these protocols are critical to ensure successful participation of the victims in investigating the crime.

Next Step #5: Appropriate protective shelter and services are critical for the protection and restoration of child sex trafficking victims.

The current situation of domestic minor sex trafficking victims being placed in general population juvenile detention or being returned to the home from which they fled is detrimental to all parties. These victims require specialized care while being secured from their trafficker. The lack of such shelter across the nation is preventing first responders from succeeding in protecting and gaining justice for the victims of child sex trafficking. Funding authorized in the TVPA reauthorization for such shelters and services for domestic victims must be appropriated in order to move forward in this critical area.

Next Step #6: A nationwide, multi-disciplinary reporting measure is needed to capture the true scope of domestic minor sex trafficking.

There is no national reporting measure currently in place to provide accurate reporting of the numbers of commercially sexually exploited youth in America. The proliferation of labels and variations in data reporting in each state creates an inability to assess the true scope of domestic minor sex trafficking. Nonetheless, experts have estimated numbers from 100,000 to 300,000 children each year are victimized in prostitution in America. It is critical to establish standard reporting metrics through a federal authority in order to address this crime and victimization in a national approach. The 42 Human Trafficking Task Forces funded through the Department of Justice, Bureau of Justice Assistance have required performance metrics, which collect the statistics and information on human trafficking cases involving foreign victims. Barriers to reporting on domestic sex trafficking victims must be lifted and these numbers collected as well in order to obtain a complete picture of the scope of domestic minor sex trafficking in the United States. Additionally, child protection agencies in each state should establish a classification of commercial sexual exploitation of children in the reporting format.

Next Step #7: Survivors must be leaders in the development of services, shelter, and response protocols to domestic minor sex trafficking.

Survivor leadership is critical to establishing appropriate protections for victims of domestic minor sex trafficking, as they have shared histories and can establish trust and elicit disclosure successfully. Several effective programs and organizations are led by survivors currently and these should be supported further to be more effective. Survivors are excellent advocates and must be facilitated in being heard at the policy level.

Shared Hope's Next Step:

The Protected Innocence Initiative

Since the Trafficking Victims Protection Act became law in the year 2000, sex trafficking of minors who are U.S. citizens or legal permanent residents has been recognized as a federal crime. While the intent of this law and its reauthorizations in 2005 and 2008 is exemplary, it has done little to protect the innocence of America's children. One of the primary explanations for this failure is that each state has its own set of definitions, laws, and policies that often fail to address the crime of commercial sexual exploitation of a child.

Our findings in the National Report on Domestic Minor Sex Trafficking clearly call for a holistic strategy that promotes zero tolerance for child sex trafficking at the level of state law. Shared Hope International launched such a strategy — called the Protected Innocence Initiative — that addresses at least the first three imperatives of the Next Steps document. This initiative calls for the release of fifty-one individual Report Cards based on the Protected Innocence Legislative Framework, an analysis of state laws performed by the American Center for Law & Justice and Shared Hope International. The Report Cards set a national standard of protection against domestic minor sex trafficking. Recognizing that responses to domestic minor sex trafficking must originate at the state level, the Protected Innocence Initiative has established the base policies needed in each state to create a safe environment for children. (Please see more about the Protected Innocence Initiative in the Additional Information section of this book and at www.sharedhope.org.)

Additional Information and Resources

THE NATIONAL REPORT ON

DOMESTIC MINOR SEX TRAFFICKING
America's Prostituted Children

May 2009
Excerpt from Executive Summary

Domestic minor sex trafficking (DMST) is the commercial sexual exploitation of American children within U.S. borders. It is the "recruitment, harboring, transportation, provision, or obtaining of a person for the purpose of a commercial sex act" where the person is a U.S. citizen or lawful permanent resident under the age of 18 years.[1] The age of the victim is the critical issue — there is no requirement to prove force, fraud, or coercion was used to secure the victim's actions. In fact, the law recognizes the effect of psychological manipulation by the trafficker, as well as the effect of threat of harm which traffickers/pimps use to maintain control over their young victims.[2] DMST includes but is not limited to the commercial sexual exploitation of children through prostitution, pornography, and/or stripping. Experts estimate at

---

[1] Trafficking Victims Protection Act (TVPA) of 2000, Pub. L. No. 106-386, Division A, § 103(8), (9), 114 Stat. 1464 (signed into law on October 29, 2000); codified as amended at 22 USC 7102 § 103(8), (9). http://frwebgate.access.gpo.gov/cgi-bin/getdoc.cgi?dbname=106_cong_public_ laws& docid=f:publ386.106. Accessed on April 8, 2009.

[2] Id. at §1591(b)(2).

least 100,000 American juveniles are victimized through prostitution in America each year. Domestic minor sex trafficking is child sex slavery, child sex trafficking, prostitution of children, commercial sexual exploitation of children (CSEC), and rape of a child.

Shared Hope International first actively addressed the sex trafficking of American children through research on the markets that create demand for commercial sex and which result in the commercial sexual exploitation of women and girls. The DEMAND. Project investigated buyers, facilitators, and traffickers in four countries: Jamaica, Japan, the Netherlands, and the United States. The startling findings highlighted the fact that sex trafficking is demand-driven and the product for sale is most commonly local (domestic) children. Dedicated to ending the human rights violation of sex trafficking internationally and domestically, Shared Hope International received a grant from the U.S. Department of Justice to perform field research on domestic minor sex trafficking — the commercial sexual exploitation of American children in the United States.

Acknowledging that strategic responses to sex trafficking require comprehensive understanding of the local situation, Shared Hope International aligned with the U.S. Department of Justice-funded human trafficking task forces to assess domestic minor sex trafficking and the access to victim services in ten U.S. locations:

1. Dallas, TX
2. San Antonio, TX
3. Fort Worth, TX
4. Salt Lake City, UT
5. Buffalo, NY
6. Baton Rouge and New Orleans, LA
7. Independence, MO
8. Las Vegas, NV
9. Clearwater, FL
10. The Commonwealth of the Northern Mariana Islands (U.S. Territory)

The assessment process investigated the three areas of Prevention, Prosecution, and Protection ("three Ps") as the key components necessary to effectively combat trafficking in persons. The assessments involved qualitative interviews of professionals likely to come into contact with victims of domestic minor sex trafficking, as well as quantitative data collection when available. Seven professional groups were identified as likely to come into contact with victims of domestic minor sex trafficking and targeted for interviews: Federal, State, and Local Law Enforcement; Federal and State Prosecutors; Juvenile Court; Juvenile Probation and Detention; Public Defenders; Child Protective Services; and Social Services/Non-Governmental Organizations. A total of 297 interviews were conducted. Statistics were requested but were not always available. In many cases, statistics provided did not disaggregate data on domestic minor sex trafficking — a term and crime most interviewees were not familiar with yet; in these cases the statistics were reviewed for extrapolation in determining numbers of suspected domestic minor sex trafficking victims. For example, juvenile detention facility statistics reflecting numbers of youth detained under charges of prostitution could be properly counted toward the number of domestic minor sex trafficking victims in that facility as juveniles in prostitution are victims of sex trafficking under the federal Trafficking Victims Protection Act of 2000 (TVPA). The reliance on extrapolated data reflects the glaring lack of identification of domestic minor sex trafficking victims and highlights the need for training as well as data collection on this victim population.

Each assessed location produced information that was documented in an area-specific report, including information on the scope of the problem, how victims of domestic minor sex trafficking were accessing the system, how they were being labeled, and, as a result of that label, how victims of domestic minor sex trafficking were accessing or being barred from accessing services as victims of a violent crime. The findings from the 10 site assessments, research studies, and field work are the foundation for this National Report on the Identification and Response to America's Trafficked Youth. Substantiation of the findings was gained through Shared Hope International's National Training Conference on the Sex Trafficking of America's Youth held

September 15-16, 2008, in Dallas, Texas, which brought together nearly 200 first responders from across the nation to share their experiences and best practices for responding to domestic minor sex trafficking. Also, experts on the trauma and services required to counteract the trauma endured provided guidance in forming best practices in this field.

End of excerpt.

Summary of Findings:

Victims of domestic minor sex trafficking can be found in every city, town, and community in our country, but for a variety of reasons, they are seen as the problem, not as children <u>with</u> a problem. The reasons can be summarized as follows:

1. Misidentification

Our research found misidentification of the victims to be the primary barrier to rescue and response. Misidentification occurs at all levels of first responders and causes a chain reaction of negative outcomes. It is responsible for the failure to deliver the necessary services to interrupt and treat the trauma the child has endured. Misidentification can be remedied only through awareness and education of first responders and the community at large to recognize the indicators of domestic minor sex trafficking and to respond with appropriate treatment developed by experts in this specific form of trauma.

2. Criminalization of the Victim

Victims of domestic minor sex trafficking are frequently viewed by law enforcement as juvenile delinquents or adult prostitutes. Prostituted juveniles are trained by their trafficker/pimp to lie to authorities and are provided with excellent fraudulent identification resulting in their arrest records as adults. Those who are identified as minors are frequently charged with a delinquent act either for prostitution or for an offense such as drug possession or habitual runaway. These children are found in detention facilities across the country, often as the only option to keep them safe for a time from the pimp. Others are placed in juvenile justice rehabilitative programs, but due to the unique trauma bonding that occurs between a victim and her trafficker, these children often run from juvenile facilities right back to the person that exploited them.

3. Burden on the Victim to build the Case Against the Trafficker/Pimp

Arrest and prosecution of the trafficker is too frequently based solely on the victim's cooperation and testimony. This approach places a burden on the victim — a burden that is most often too heavy for these traumatized children who typically require a lengthy amount of time and the use of advanced interview techniques in order to disclose.

4. Inappropriate Services/No Therapeutic Shelters for DMST Trauma Victims

Experts speak of the trauma suffered by child sex trafficking victims as more severe than most sexually-based trauma given the chronic nature coupled with the reinforced victimization from the community of buyers. Therefore, the services required for a child sex trafficking victim are unique and rarely available. There are very few residential shelters in the entire U.S. that serve this population of victims.

5. Insufficient Priority on Combating Demand

Buyers are not being recognized as a critical component in the sex trafficking of children; yet demand is the primary driver of the commercial sex industry within which children are being exploited for commercial sex activities. If there was no buyer, there would be no trafficker — and certainly no victim!

PROTECTED INNOCENCE INITIATIVE
Creating A Uniform Standard Across States to Combat Domestic Minor Sex Trafficking

Introduction

The Protected Innocence Legislative Framework is based on research performed by Shared Hope International and compiled in "The National Report on Domestic Minor Sex Trafficking." Domestic minor sex trafficking is the prostitution, pornography, or sexual performance of U.S. citizens or lawful permanent residents under the age of 18 in the United States.

Recognizing that most of the gaps in responding to domestic minor sex trafficking must be addressed at the state level, the Protected Innocence Framework sets out the basic policy principles required to create a safe environment for children. The steps necessary to create this safe environment include: prevention of domestic minor sex trafficking through reducing demand; rescue and restoration of victims through improved training on identification; establishment of protocols and facilities for placements; mandating appropriate services and shelter; and incorporating trauma-reducing mechanisms into the justice system. Broken systems of response to victims must also be fixed to ensure that the commercially sexually exploited children are treated as victims and provided with remedies through the law to recapture their lives and their futures.

Four primary policy issues must be addressed in order to combat domestic minor sex trafficking: 1) eliminating demand; 2) prosecuting traffickers; 3) identifying victims; and 4) providing protection, access to services, and shelter for victims.

1. Eliminating Demand. Despite the fact that demand is the primary driver of the commercial sex industry and the commercial sexual exploitation of children, buyers are often not recognized as a critical component in the victimization of children through domestic minor sex trafficking. All buyers of sex with children—whether they be classified as preferential (pedophiles), opportunistic (thrill seekers), or situational (do not care how old the person being prostituted is) — are committing a crime.

2. Prosecuting Traffickers. Frequently, the arrest and prosecution of the trafficker is based solely on the victim's cooperation in the investigation and testimony at trial. This approach, however, can place a heavy burden on a domestic minor sex trafficking victim, who typically requires a lengthy amount of time before they will disclose the facts of their victimization. Therefore, it is critical for law enforcement officers to pursue innovative and/or alternative investigation techniques to corroborate the victims' allegations in domestic minor sex trafficking cases.

3. Identifying Victims. Misidentification of victims is the primary barrier to victim rescue and law enforcement response to domestic minor sex trafficking. It causes a chain reaction of negative outcomes, the most significant of which is the failure to deliver the necessary services to interrupt and treat the trauma these children have endured. The problem occurs at all levels of first response from law enforcement arrests on the street, to the intake processes of homeless and runaway youth shelters, to court adjudication of victims as juvenile delinquents for offenses committed in connection with the prostitution of the child. The adjudication of the victim as a delinquent and detention in juvenile facilities is a too frequent outcome. Law enforcement reported another barrier to proper identification is that prostituted juveniles are trained by their trafficker to lie to authorities and are provided with excellent fraudulent identification. This results in their registration in the arrest records as an adult — an identification that follows them through their years as a minor unless and until it is corrected by the insight of a law enforcement officer who recognizes that the victim is a minor and pursues a correct identification. The use of high risk indicator tools that would flag chronic runaways and other status offenders as likely victims of domestic minor sex trafficking would greatly improve the identification process.

4. Providing Protection, Access to Services, and Shelter for Victims. Law enforcement officers expressed frustration with the fact that they are often compelled to charge a domestic minor sex trafficking victim with a delinquency offense, such as prostitution, in order to detain her and to keep her safe from the trafficker. Detention, however, is detrimental to the victim in that she rarely receives any services in detention, much less services specific to the trauma endured through sex trafficking. Due to the unique trauma bonding that occurs between a victim and her trafficker, these children often run from juvenile facilities right back to the person that exploited them. Also, in some states, a victim's entry into the delinquency system can disqualify her from accessing victim of crime funds for services. The establishment of protective shelters and services for domestic minor sex trafficking victims would provide law enforcement officers or juvenile courts with an alternative placement for prostituted minors. Protective shelters also provide a more conducive environment for breaking the cycle of destructive trauma bonding between a victim and her trafficker and restoring a victim to the point where she can assist in an investigation and trial. Despite the need for protective shelters, less than one hundred beds in facilities appropriate for and specializing in treating domestic minor sex trafficking victims exist across the country. Establishing these protective shelters is critical for creating an effective strategy to combat domestic minor sex trafficking.

Methodology

The purpose of the Protected Innocence Legislative Framework is to elaborate key policy principles that are critical to making the proper response to domestic minor sex trafficking. These can be grouped into six areas of law:

- Criminalization of Domestic Minor Sex Trafficking Statutes
- Criminal Provisions for Demand
- Criminal Provisions for Traffickers

- Criminal Provisions for Facilitators
- Protective Provisions for the Child Victims
- Law Enforcement and Criminal Justice Tools to Effectuate Investigation and Prosecutions

Each area of law may have several laws that impact the policy within the state's code. As such, specific questions must be asked to determine the sufficiency of a state's laws to address the policy need.

[NOTE: A total of 40 different points of law are examined under these six major areas of law. The entire methodology can be found at www.sharedhope.org.]

A letter grade will reflect the level of protections, actions, and remedies available in a domestic minor sex trafficking case in the respective state. A short analysis of the legislation of each state will follow with recommendations.

It is important to note that the methodology looks solely at the laws in place in a given state and their de jure compliance with the Protected Innocence Legislative Framework at the time of the review. This analysis does not review the enforcement or implementation of the laws, though clearly enforcement is of critical importance.
End of excerpt.

Please visit www.sharedhope.org to find complete information about the Protected Innocence Initiative and the report cards for each state as they are completed.

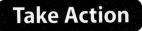

You can do all of this at www.sharedhope.org!

1. Learn more. Go online to read about the Protected Innocence Initiative in your state.

2. Sign petitions. Watch for Shared Hope International's online petitions regarding upcoming federal and state legislative initiatives.

3. Train first responders. Access our online resources that help train law enforcement, social service providers and other first responders to assist victims of sex-trafficking.

4. Raise awareness. Utilize Shared Hope materials to Host Your Own Event and spread the word about sex trafficking in your community. Call 1-866-HER-LIFE for more information.

5. Share her story. View the informative video, "Do You Know Lacy?" on our website and share it with friends. Give a copy of *Renting Lacy* to one other person or a school library.

6. Join The Defenders USA. Men, find out actions you can take to defend her; wear a shirt that tells the story.

7. Donate. Give generously of your resources (finances, time, talents or connections) to help us end sex slavery in our day.

8. Stand with us. Join us on Facebook (http://www.facebook.com/sharedhopeinternational) or Twitter to help us continue to lead the fight against sex trafficking.